Britain beneath ou

An atlas of digital information on Britain's land quality, underground hazards, resources and geology

Bibliographic reference

JACKSON, I (editor). 2004.
Britain beneath our feet. *(Keyworth, Nottingham: British Geological Survey Occasional Publication No. 4.)*

Giant's Causeway, County Antrim, Northern Ireland

Britain beneath our feet

Contents

Whin Gill, Eskdale, Cumbria

Britain beneath our feet

Foreword

I didn't know you did that! This is a phrase we hear frequently from our visitors and one that has prompted the production of this atlas. We hope the atlas will bring to your attention the wealth of digital data and information that is held by the British Geological Survey — the custodian of the nation's geoscientific information.

When I joined the British Geological Survey (BGS) in 1997, I was amazed at the extent and depth of information that exists within the organisation. Perhaps I shouldn't have been, after all the Geological Survey has been around since 1835. But at the same time, I was, and am, saddened because that information is still not used to its full potential to improve the health and wealth of the nation.

Geology is a science that is relevant to the everyday lives of us all. Unfortunately many people, including many in positions of power in the commercial, industrial and political world, do not fully appreciate this. The role of geology in ensuring environmental protection, sustainable development and a safer world is not widely understood. In recent years, BGS has been trying to play its part in addressing this. We have devoted our resources to undertaking scientific research and developing products and services that attempt to meet the real needs of our users. Many of our new users are not geologists, and this atlas, like many of our other new products, has been written with this in mind, avoiding as far as possible the use of unnecessary technical terms.

It is an understatement to say that many of our newest developments would not have been possible without the revolution in information technology. This has provided geoscientists with new digital tools in the form of powerful databases, *Geographical Information Systems* and three-dimensional modelling software — tools that allow us to reach out and try to meet the needs of our users.

This first edition of the atlas shows how digital information now permeates the geosciences. But geoscience and information technology are dynamic and this atlas can be only a snapshot in time. In the next few years BGS will continue to invest in extending and improving the information you see here and a new edition will be needed.

I hope that you will find both the atlas and accompanying interactive web site and CD_ROM enlightening and useful, and that it will raise your awareness of the pervasiveness and relevance of geology to everyday life. But this atlas gives only a glimpse of what BGS can offer. Underpinning the data and information store are the expertise and knowledge of the 515 geoscientists who work in the BGS. Should you have questions or comments about the information you see here, contact us; we will be delighted to help you use this resource to its fullest extent.

Dr David Falvey,
Executive Director
February 2004

The Green Bridge of Wales, Pembrokeshire

Britain beneath our feet

Introduction

We live on a piece of the Earth's crust that has had an immensely long and eventful history, some of it shrouded in mystery. The land we now know as Britain has travelled the globe, and more than once it has lain at the bottom of the ocean. The ground beneath us has been buried to red-hot depths, broken apart by earthquakes and frozen under glaciers, emerging as the unique landscape we know today.

This landscape may be seen as a stage on which we act out the conflicts inherent in all land-use. It is a source of mineral wealth and water, but it may also be seen as a location for a major engineering project or a receptacle for rubbish. Government and industrialists may look at the landscape and see the challenge of combining mineral extraction with a respect for the environment. Increasingly, the public will have a view on these matters too, but may also simply wish to understand the land they live in — why is my soil light or heavy, acid or limy: what made that hill in the distance: why is there a spring here?

At the beginning of the 21st century, the expectation is that information about the landscape should be available in computer-readable (digital) form. We need to make the information as accessible as possible for use in a whole variety of software, from deceptively simple Internet browsers to sophisticated *Geographical Information Systems* and database programs, and it must be available via the World Wide Web.

We are publishing this atlas as a brief introduction to the wealth of digital data, information and knowledge that the British Geological Survey holds on the land beneath our feet — knowledge that can help us all to address the questions above.

Whatever we may feel about the economic, environmental and aesthetic costs and benefits of our future plans for this landscape, there cannot be an informed decision without knowledge of what is there.

Thumbnail map of data coverage

54

Hazards

Swelling and shrinking clay

Some clays increase or decrease in volume as they absorb or lose water. These volume changes can cause, either swelling (heave) or shrinking (subsidence). In rocks that contain clay, the amount of volume change will depend on both the amount and the type of clay minerals present because some clays can absorb more water than others with a proportionally greater effect.

Inset showing detailed data

The map indicates the *potential* for shrinking or swelling of the ground to be a hazard. The problem is most widespread in southern and eastern England where young clay rich rocks are at or near the surface.

Detailed information on the location and extent of swelling and shrinking clays is relevant to planners, landowners, engineers and householders and to those in the property transaction and insurance sectors. In areas where swelling and shrinking clays are a problem, foundations should be set sufficiently deeply to avoid the active shrink-swell zone and should be designed to resist lateral swelling pressures. Before planting or removing trees and shrubs near buildings sited in areas with significant shrink swell potential it is advisable to seek professional advice.

Swelling and shrinking clay potential has been assessed using 1:50 000 scale maps of bedrock geology and superficial deposits, combined with information from several hundred thousand borehole records, scientific documents and engineering reports, photographs and geotechnical property values from the *National Geotechnical Properties Database*. The detailed digital data is available as attributed vector polygons, raster grids, and in spread sheet format.

Text describing the theme, its uses and the detailed source data

Photograph reproduced with permission of NHBC

Photograph reproduced with permission of NHBC

Britain beneath our feet

A guide to the atlas

This atlas is divided into five sections:

Base data

Land quality and groundwater

Hazards

Resources

Offshore and coastal

Each of the sections is presented as a series of themes. Each theme occupies a double-page spread and is illustrated with a map of either onshore UK, or the UK Continental Shelf Designated Area. The information shown on these maps represents small-scale generalisations, an overview of much more detailed digital information that is available from the British Geological Survey (BGS). A key on each map explains the colours and symbols used, but note that this key applies to the generalised map only.

The page facing the map consists of a number of elements. There is a description of the theme, the uses it has and information about the detailed source data from which it was derived. Small 'thumbnail' maps illustrate the extent of the coverage of the detailed, high-resolution information that BGS holds. An inset map shows what that detailed information looks like at full resolution. On some pages we have also used tables and graphs to illustrate a particular point.

To accompany the book, BGS will be releasing an interactive CD_ROM and internet site. These will contain all of the material in the atlas, and also allow the user to search and interrogate the data, to look at the separate components of the individual themes or to combine them. More information on the detailed digital data and relevant contact addresses are given on page 111.

Salisbury Crags, Edinburgh

Britain beneath our feet

Base data

Data described in this section largely form the basis of the other themes within this atlas. Thus, the composition, age, thickness and form of the surface and bedrock geology are key building blocks of themes within the sections on *Land quality and groundwater, Hazards* and *Resources*. Similarly, gravity and magnetic data play an important role in elucidating the deeper structure of our country and its mineral resources.

The themes in this section in turn depend on 'raw' data not featured individually within this atlas. Included are borehole logs, rock samples, fossil and mineral specimens, seismic lines, individual gravity and magnetic readings and a wealth of other data.

The BGS National Geoscience Data Centre (NGDC) is the place where all the data are held. The borehole database, one component of the NGDC, now numbers over one million logs and is growing at an average rate of 50 000 logs per year. All borehole logs have been scanned and are now held in digital form. Some 100 000 kilometres of seismic line data are held by the NGDC. The materials collection holds over 200 kilometres of drill core and one million borehole samples (which, together with the drillcore, represents over 3000 kilometres of drilling), one million rock and mineral samples and three million fossil specimens. The majority of this data are digitally catalogued and the index information can be accessed online at *www.bgs.ac.uk/geoindex/home.html*.

1:250 000 scale data

1:50 000 scale data

1:10 000 scale data

Base data

Surface geology

A veneer of soil, concrete and tarmac conceals the underlying geological foundation of Britain. In many areas that foundation starts with several metres of clay and silt, or sand and gravel – the 'Superficial Deposits'- predominantly a product of the last Ice Age and river action since then. However, the underlying 'bedrock' is seldom far from the surface, especially in the mountains. In the south of Britain, a part of the country that was beyond the limits of the glaciers, Superficial Deposits are often absent and bedrock directly underlies the soil and concrete.

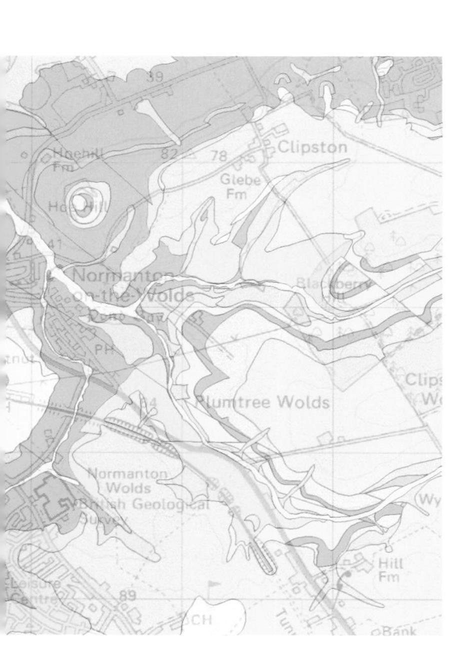

The composition of the bedrock (solid) and superficial deposits (drift) is the major factor that determines the landscape of Britain. The rugged topography of the Lake District and Snowdonia is due to hard sedimentary and volcanic rocks; soft clay, silt and peat give the characteristic form to the Vale of York and The Fens; the rolling hills of the Cotswolds and the North and South Downs owe their existence to the underlying Jurassic limestone and Cretaceous chalk. The influence of geology on terrain, drainage and soil type is not difficult to see.

But an understanding of the composition and origin of rocks has many more uses than appreciating Britain's scenery. Knowledge of the distribution of the rocks and their physical and chemical composition is critical to environmental protection, civil engineering, mineral and water resource exploitation, and in the management and control of natural hazards. Information on the composition of the rocks and sediments at and close to the land surface — the zone in which we live and work — is the fundamental information that underpins many of the other themes in this atlas.

The map opposite is a generalisation of much more detailed source information. The geology of the UK is surveyed at a scale of 1:10 000 and maps are published at 1:50 000 scale. This information is now available in digital form *(BGS-DigMapGB)*. This database is in *Geographical Information System* format and holds the spatial (vector) data and linked geological attributes. The database is being added to daily. Currently it contains more than 400 000 units of different *Bedrock* and *Superficial Deposits*, and provides comprehensive coverage of the country.

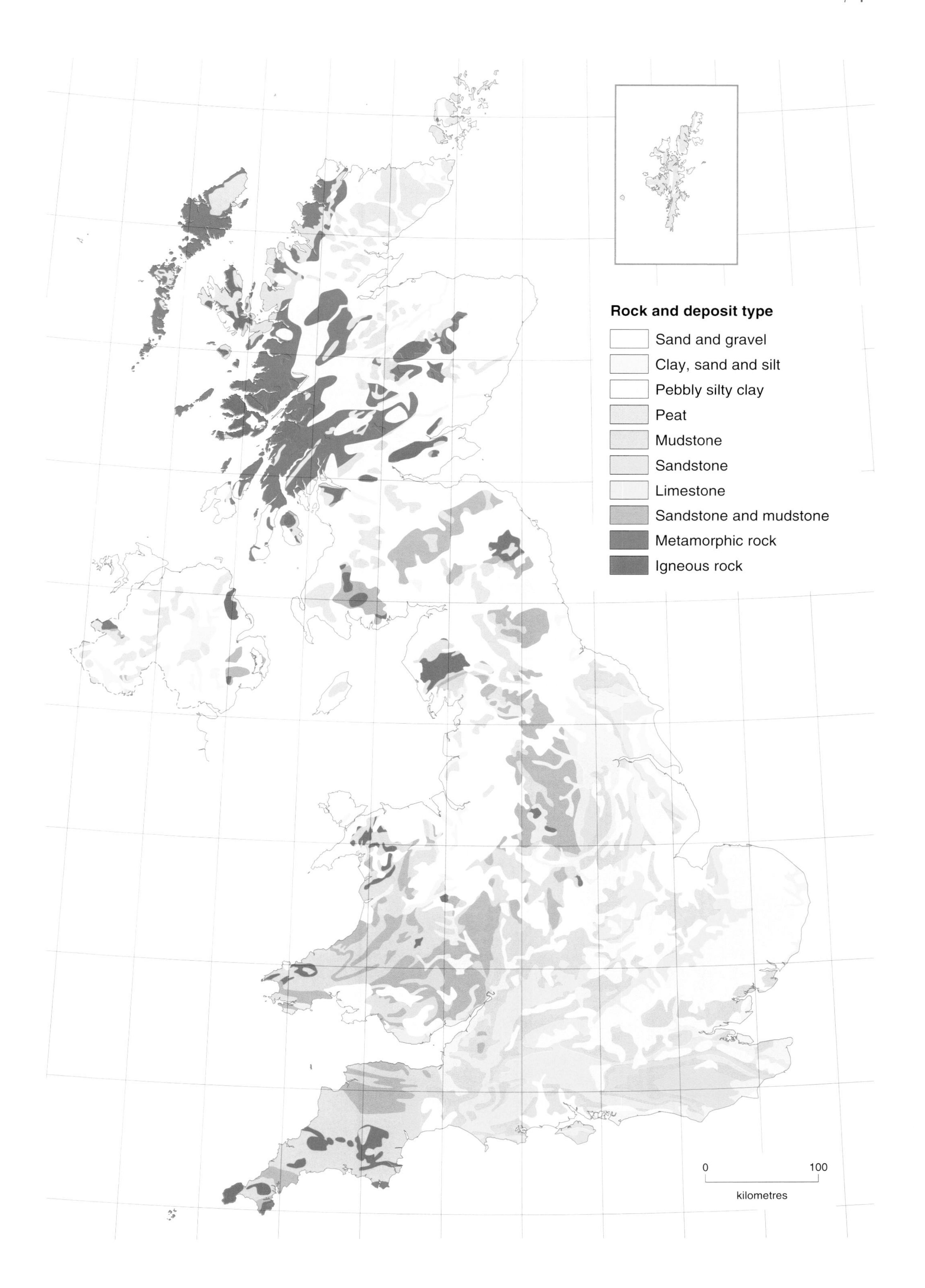
Rock and deposit type
Sand and gravel
Clay, sand and silt
Pebbly silty clay
Peat
Mudstone
Sandstone
Limestone
Sandstone and mudstone
Metamorphic rock
Igneous rock
0
100
kilometres

Base data

Thickness of Superficial Deposits

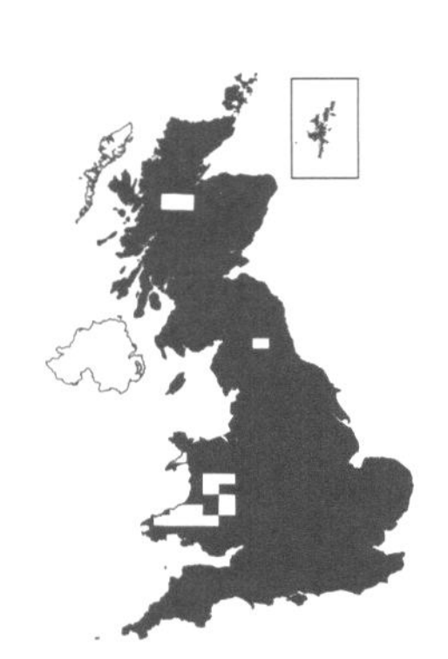

Superficial Deposits are the youngest of the geological formations (less than 2 million years old) and cover much of the bedrock of Britain. They are largely unconsolidated and include man-made material such as coal tips and quarry infill.

Even at the scale of 1:4.25 million, the map clearly highlights the extensive thick glacial and post-glacial deposits of Cheshire, Tees-side, East Anglia and the Yorkshire – Humberside coast.

The thickness of Superficial Deposits and the related dataset that shows the height of the bedrock surface are critical parameters in a number of areas of work. For example, in civil engineering (planning and building of roads, pipelines and major structures), in the evaluation of groundwater resources and their potential for pollution, and as a key input to the prediction of surface hazards such as landslides and the collapse of underlying rocks.

The map is a mathematical model of the thickness of the Superficial Deposits produced by analysing information from approximately 600 000 borehole logs held in the BGS archives and also uses digital data on the extent of Superficial Deposits (see page 6). Until now most large-scale models showing the thickness of Superficial Deposits have covered only restricted areas and have been produced manually, and any nation-wide models are usually very small scale and schematic. The latter also tend to generalise thickness and rely on intuitive or preconceived views of thickness variation. The detailed digital data for this model are in the form of an interpolated grid with a resolution of 50 × 50 metres.

This thickness model is intended to act as a starting point for more sophisticated analyses of the Superficial Deposits of Britain, and further enhancements are planned to improve its quality and spatial coverage.

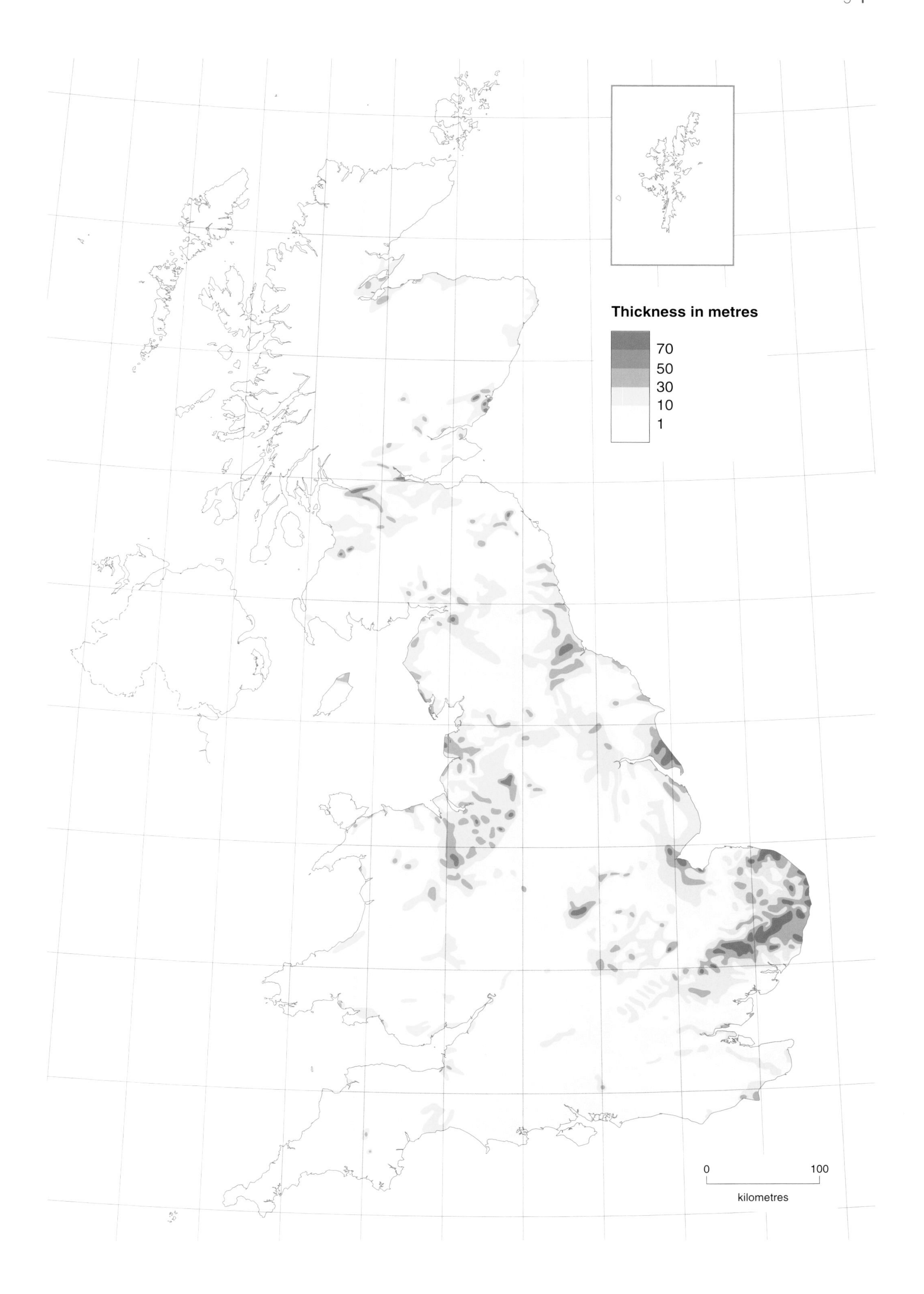
Thickness in metres
70
50
30
10
1
0
100
kilometres

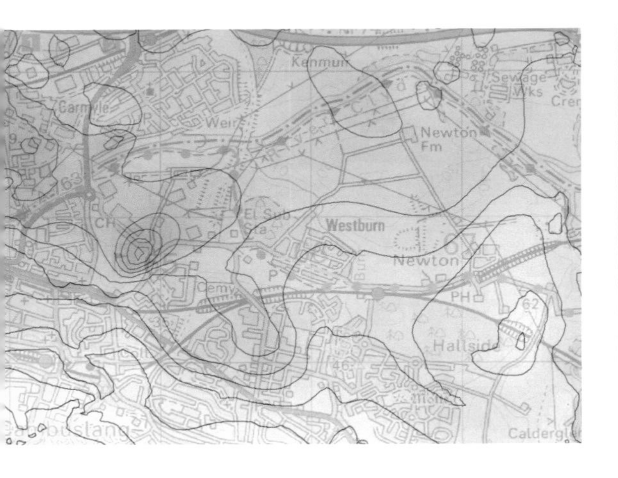

Base data

Height of the bedrock surface

Commonly known as rockhead elevation, the map shows the height of the bedrock surface above mean sea level. In many areas the bedrock surface is similar to, or closely mirrors, the height of the ground surface. In other places it is completely different because of the presence of Superficial Deposits.

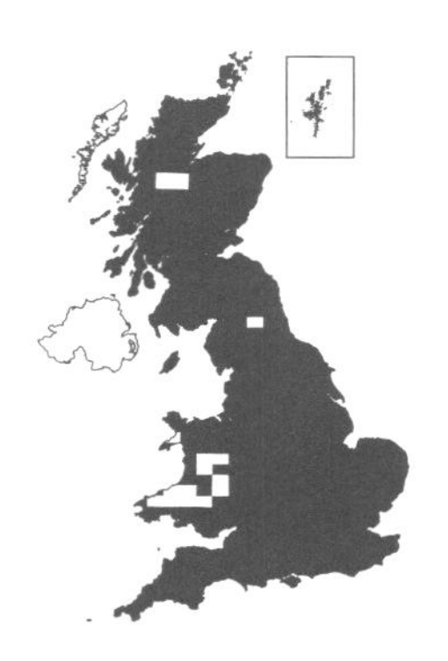

In several places along the east coast of England, and perhaps most notably in the Vale of York and around The Wash, the surface can be seen to be many metres below present sea level. Many such differences become apparent in the detailed dataset.

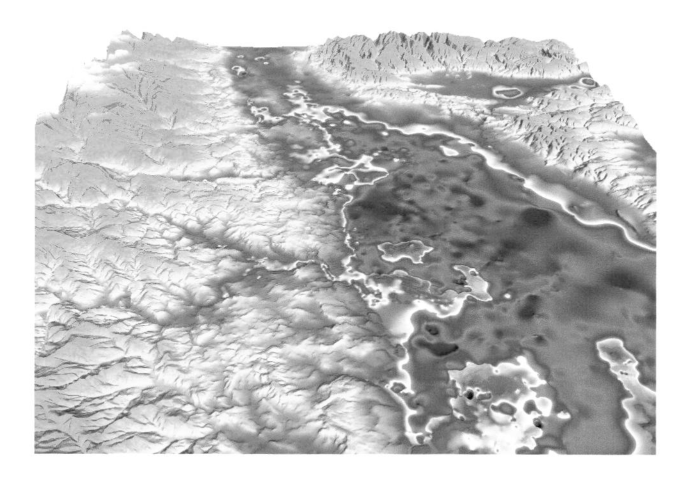

The elevation of the bedrock surface has similar applications to the dataset for the thickness of Superficial Deposits. The two datasets are closely related; each of these parameters is iteratively involved in the calculation of the other. The ability to predict rockhead surface and to understand its shape and form is important in engineering and construction, as well as in the assessment of the likelihood and effect of underground hazards.

The detailed data that underlie the generalised map opposite are in the form of an interpolated grid with a resolution of 50 × 50 metres. Again, the model is produced from processing borehole information, geological map data and a model of the ground surface. It is a repeatable mathematical model; this avoids potentially subjective geomorphological analysis of the data, but is weaker in areas of poor data density where the BGS archives hold no information, and mathematical trends may not reflect likely geological features. Future versions of the model will be enhanced by geologically based regional reviews and conceptual models derived from local and regional knowledge.

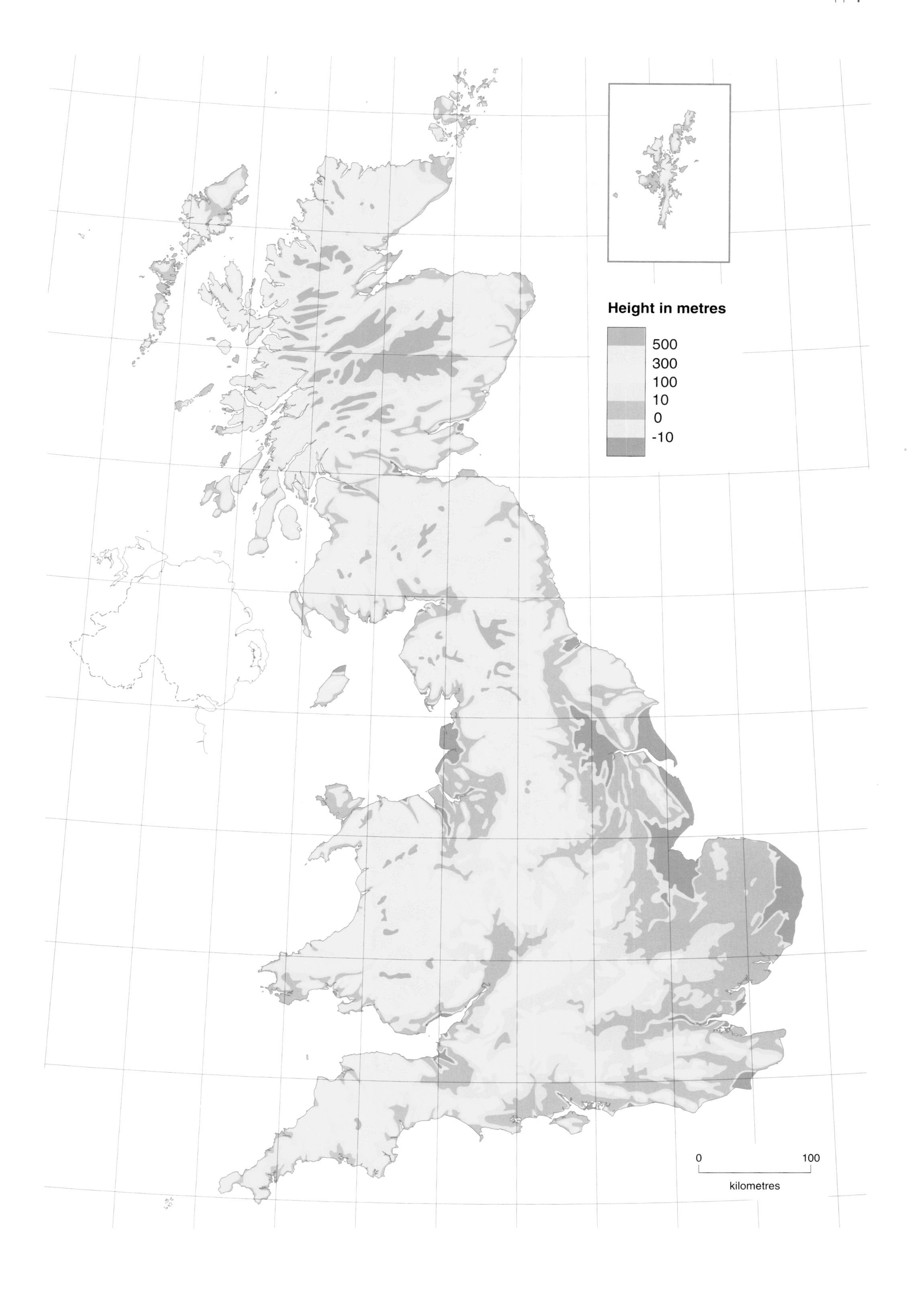
Height in metres
500
300
100
10
0
-10
0
100
kilometres

1:250 000 scale data

1:50 000 scale data

1:10 000 scale data

Base data

Bedrock age

Stripping away the widespread blanket of unconsolidated material — the Superficial Deposits deposited by glaciers and rivers in the last two million years — would reveal the bedrock of Britain. The Earth is over 4600 million years old. The oldest rocks in Britain are the Precambrian rocks of the Northwest Highlands of Scotland, and are around 3000 million years old. In general, as one travels south and east in the UK, the bedrock becomes younger, so that the London Clay, deposited about 50 million years ago, is one of the youngest formations in Britain.

Britain has a very diverse geological heritage with rocks representing almost every period in Earth's history. The age of these rocks is determined from the fossils they contain or by analyses of the physical and chemical make-up. Understanding the sequence of the rocks, their relative position in a complex vertical succession, and combining this with a knowledge of the composition allows geologists to classify rocks. This classification and careful description of the rocks is the basis of the traditional product of the BGS — the 1:50 000 scale printed geological map.

Information on rock age and composition (see page 14) provides the essential foundation for many other themes in this atlas, which have applications in the area of land quality assessment, hazard prediction and resource exploration. But an understanding of bedrock age and succession also provides us with facts on past environments and the transition between those environments. This knowledge provides a key to improving our understanding of issues such as climate change and the influence of subtle and more dramatic, cataclysmic events.

The information on the map opposite and the inset map showing detailed data, originates from 1:10 000 scale field mapping. The results of the BGS geologists' field surveys and desk investigations are now routinely maintained in digital form. *Geographical Information Systems* software, and related databases hold information on the location and geometry of the rocks and their scientific attributes. For example, the 1:50 000 scale digital geological map database for Britain *(DigMapGB-50)* holds information on some 400 000 bedrock polygons, with over 16 000 unique combinations that describe the age, composition and lithology of the rocks. Currently, BGS is developing systems to capture, hold and present this information fully in three dimensions.

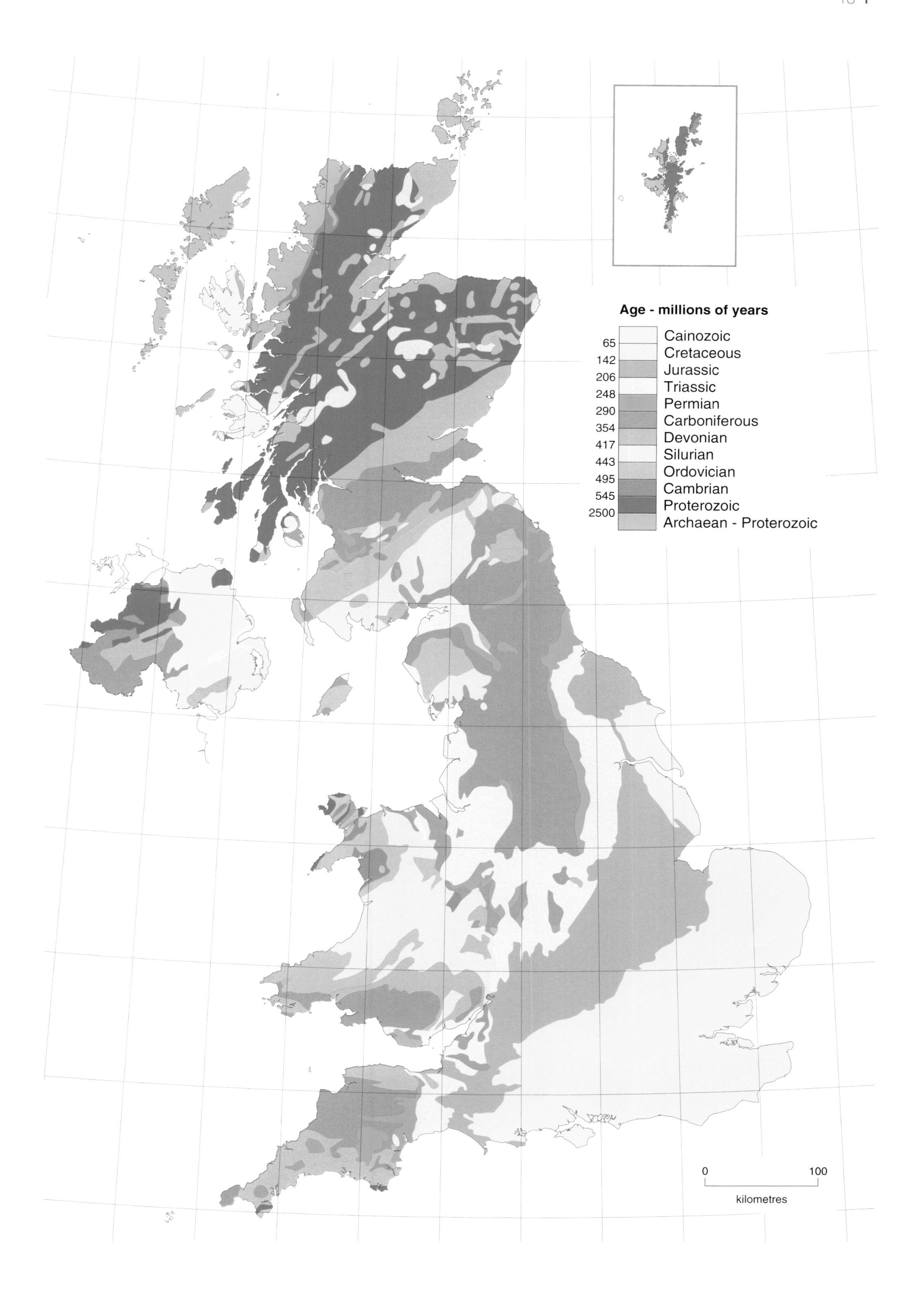
Age - millions of years
65
142
206
248
290
354
417
443
495
545
2500
Cainozoic
Cretaceous
Jurassic
Triassic
Permian
Carboniferous
Devonian
Silurian
Ordovician
Cambrian
Proterozoic
Archaean - Proterozoic
0
100
kilometres

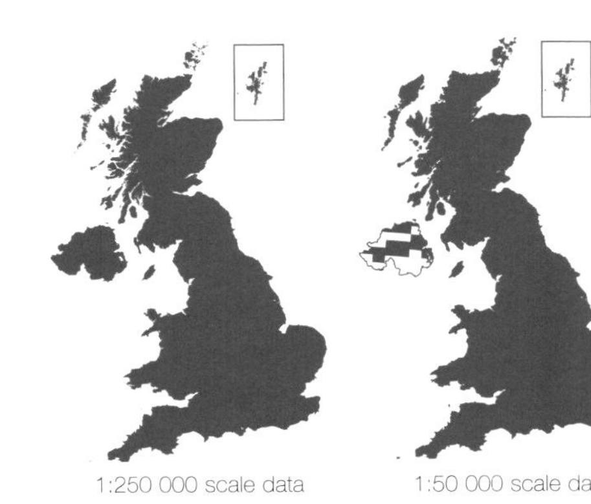

1:250 000 scale data

1:50 000 scale data

1:10 000 scale data

Base data

Bedrock geology

Bedrock is a term that is used to describe consolidated rocks. However, over much of the UK, the bedrock is concealed beneath more recent, unconsolidated material, and this map shows what the land surface of Britain would consist of if this cover were removed. Where bedrock occurs at the surface, this map is identical to the Surface Geology map shown on page 6.

The bedrock maps produced by BGS show the distribution and composition of the solid rocks. Where bedrock is not exposed at the surface an interpretation of the geology can be made from boreholes, mine plans, geophysical surveys and interpolation from adjacent areas. It is this process of interpretation that distinguishes the geological map, from a topographical map such as those produced by the Ordnance Survey. Because the geological maps are an interpretation of available data, they must be updated when new evidence becomes available or new scientific theories are established.

Understanding the configuration and properties of the bedrock is critical to many areas of our lives — construction and civil engineering, waste management, water and mineral resource extraction — the list could go on. Without an understanding of the bedrock geology of our country there can be no assurance of a safe environment or sustainable development. Other themes in this atlas draw heavily on the data described on this page.

The map opposite is a generalisation of much more detailed source information. The bedrock geology of the UK is surveyed at a scale of 1:10 000 and maps are published at 1:50 000 scale. This information is now available in digital form *(DigMapGB)*. This database is in *Geographical Information Systems* format and holds the spatial (vector) data and the linked geological attributes. The database is being added to daily. Currently the 1:50 000 scale database contains more than 400 000 units, and provides almost complete coverage of the country.

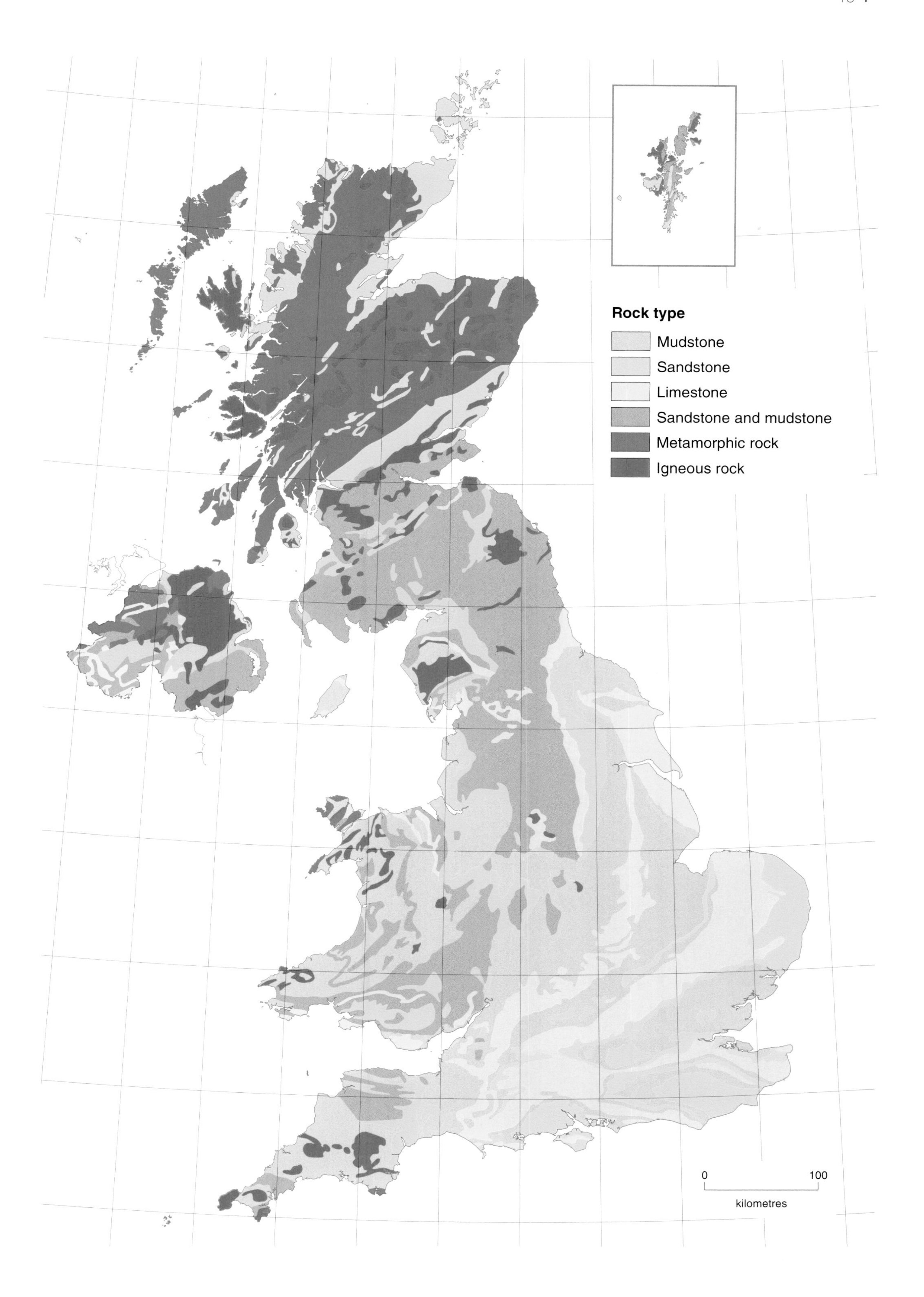
Rock type
Mudstone
Sandstone
Limestone
Sandstone and mudstone
Metamorphic rock
Igneous rock
0
100
kilometres

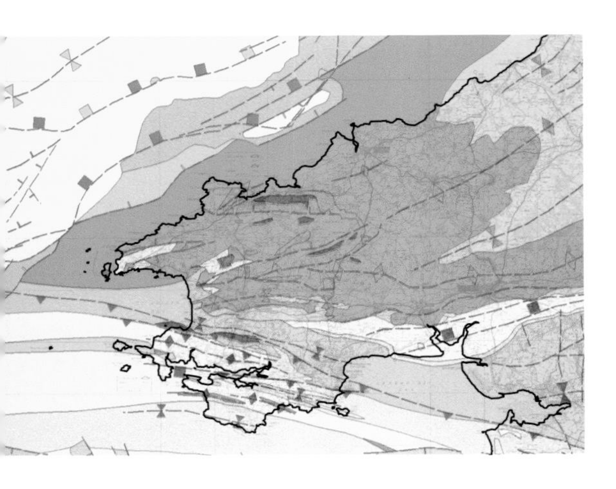

Base data

Structure of bedrock

BGS holds a vast amount of information about the deep structure of the UK. This generalised map is one small example of that information. The 'base' for the map is the Acadian unconformity; this is an extensive erosion surface that was produced about 400 million years ago, in the early Devonian, at the end of the Caledonian mountain building period. The map shows the younger strata that rest on this erosion surface, which now lies at depths of up to 10 km below the surface. Other major erosion surfaces relate to events that occurred in Carboniferous and late Cretaceous times, and similar maps can be produced showing the adjacent strata from information in our database.

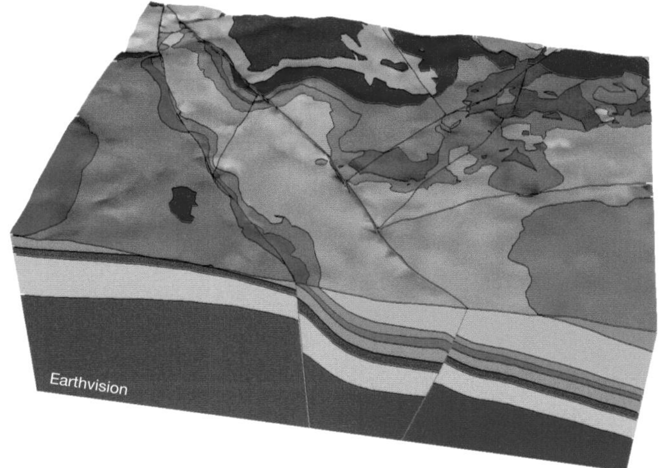

From borehole and geophysical information it is possible to provide an interpretation of the deep geological structure of Britain. The information base includes data on rock sequences, their depth, thickness, and the dislocation and deformation of these rocks (folds, faults, basins). In combination with other information it allows a comprehensive understanding of the structural evolution of the Earth's crust beneath Britain.

Such information is of use to many people, such as those from the hydrocarbon industry, who may wish to know the location and depth of sedimentary basins and the location of major faults, or from the mineral extraction industry, who may be interested in the distribution of mineralised rocks, or from the water industry, who may be concerned with the distribution of potential aquifers in the subsurface. Knowledge of the distribution of major long-lived faults also helps in monitoring earthquakes and tremors in the UK.

Data sources for these maps and interpretations are the borehole records held in the BGS borehole database (over one million boreholes are held), seismic surveys carried out principally in the search for oil and gas, analyses of gravity and magnetic surveys, and, last but not least, the detailed geological mapping undertaken by the BGS.

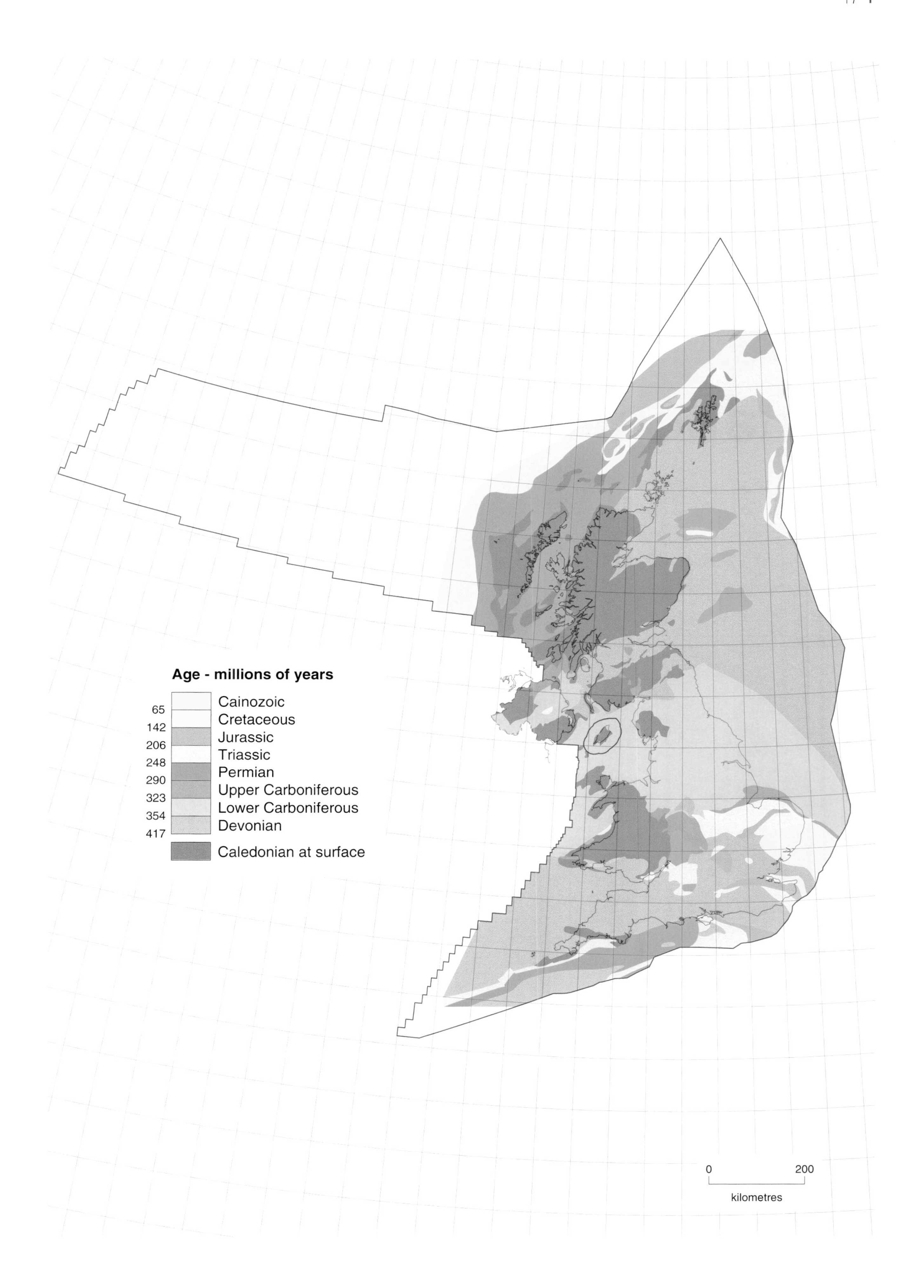
Age - millions of years
65
142
206
248
290
323
354
417
Cainozoic
Cretaceous
Jurassic
Triassic
Permian
Upper Carboniferous
Lower Carboniferous
Devonian
Caledonian at surface
0
200
kilometres

Base data

Variation in gravity field

The density of the rocks beneath our feet influences the Earth's gravity field, so we can use variations in this field to help us understand the hidden geology of Britain. This map has been generated from the large digital database of onshore and offshore gravity measurements that is held by BGS. The data can be used in investigations on scales ranging from local, near-surface features to the regional structure of the Earth's crust.

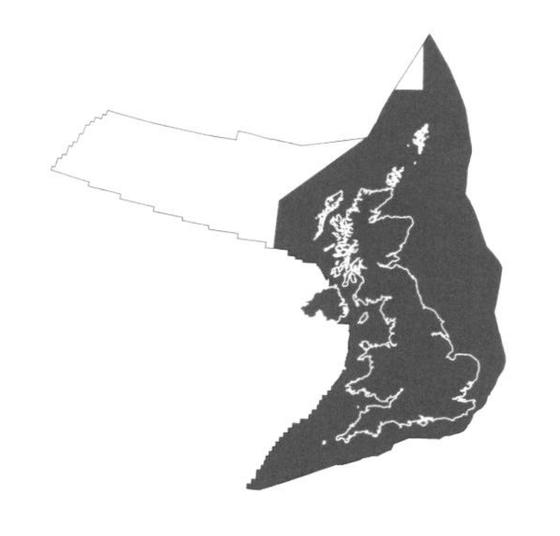

Onshore gravity measurements have been made using sensitive gravity meters at sites of known elevation throughout the country. Offshore, ship-borne gravity data have been acquired since 1967, and BGS is still active today measuring gravity at the very edge of the UK Continental Shelf. Over the oceans, the gravity field can also be determined from satellite altimetry.

The observations are corrected for factors such as station elevation and latitude, and are expressed in milligal (mGal), a unit representing about a millionth of the Earth's gravity field. Gravity lows occur over low-density bodies such as sedimentary basins and granites, whereas dense bodies such as gabbroic intrusions are associated with gravity highs. Quantitative modelling can be used to interpret the size and shape of the concealed body from its gravity expression. Special imaging methods can be used to highlight linear gravity features associated, for example, with geological faults.

Gravity surveys can be used in a wide range of studies. Detailed surveys can be used in site investigation, for example to detect underground cavities. The ability to resolve sedimentary basins makes the method valuable in oil exploration, particularly in areas where it is difficult to acquire good-quality seismic reflection data. On the broadest scale, gravity surveys help us to understand the regional configuration of the Earth's crust and upper mantle.

The digital data compilation for this map includes 167 998 gravity observations across the UK and offshore islands, tidal estuaries and sea bed, with a data point distribution of one station per 1 to 2 square kilometres. Offshore, there are 218 760 line-kilometres of BGS ship-track data with a line separation of between 5 and 15 kilometres. Satellite gravity data were derived by the Scripps Institute of Oceanography.

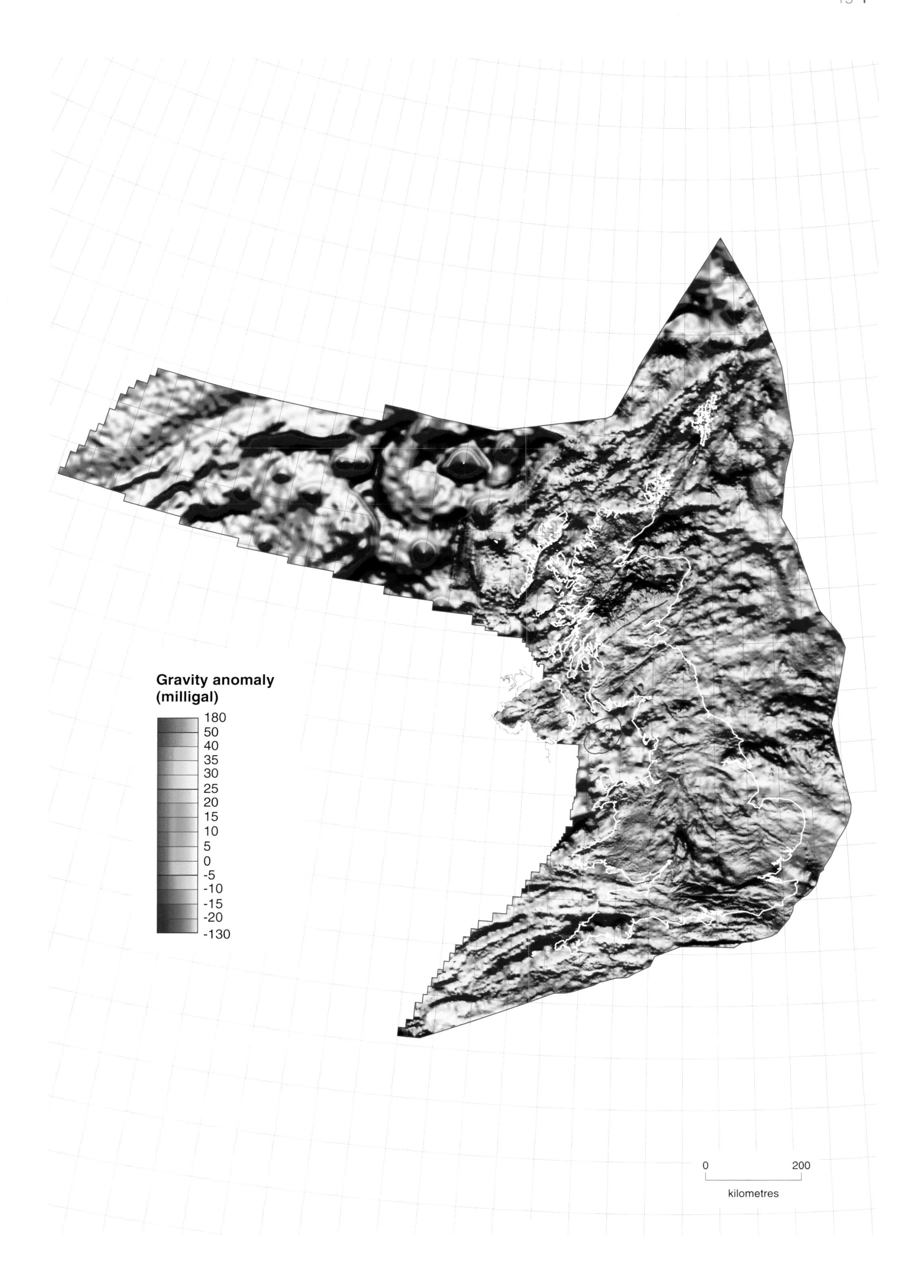
Gravity anomaly
(milligal)
180
50
40
35
30
25
20
15
10
5
0
-5
-10
-15
-20
-130
0
200
kilometres

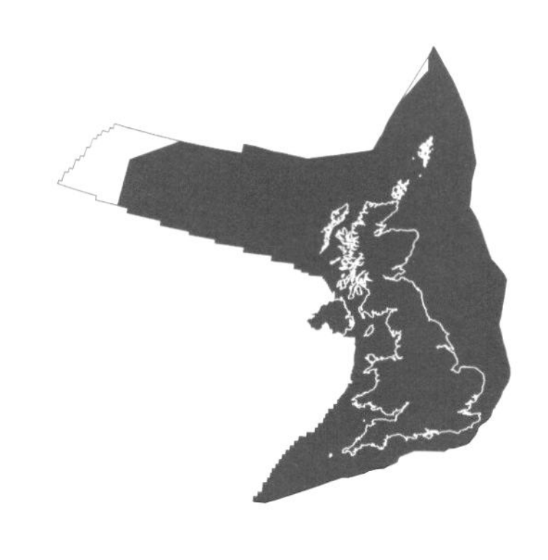

Base data

Variation in magnetic field

This map was generated from the BGS digital database of airborne and marine magnetic data, and reveals variations in the Earth's magnetic field due to contrasts in the magnetic properties of the rocks that make up its crust. Magnetic surveys provide a powerful means of mapping and modelling a variety of geological features, including igneous intrusions and structures within the concealed metamorphic basement of Britain.

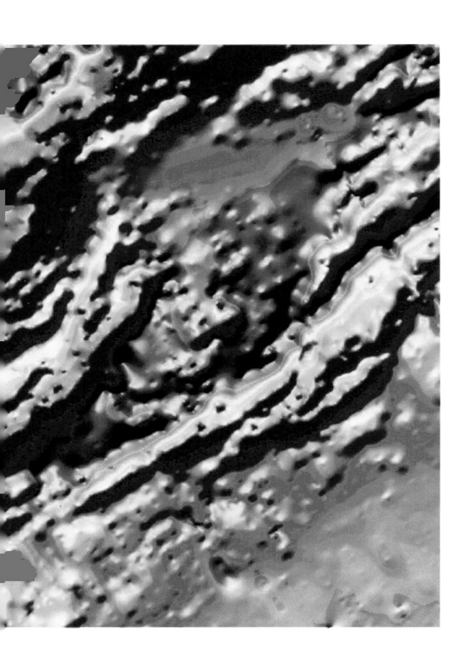

Magnetic surveys measure small departures from the expected value of the Earth's magnetic field (magnetic anomalies) caused by variations in the magnetisation of rocks within the crust. The most prominent magnetic anomalies tend to be associated with igneous and metamorphic rocks. On the map opposite, magnetic anomaly 'stripes' in the far west reflect reversals in the magnetisation of the oceanic crust, which provided key evidence in support of the concept of sea-floor spreading. The pattern over northern Britain includes anomalies due to igneous complexes and linear features due to dyke swarms and magnetic bodies bounded by faults. Farther south, anomalies over southern Britain reflect components within a geological basement that was assembled prior to the deposition of less magnetic sedimentary cover.

Magnetic surveys are used for geological mapping and mineral exploration, and on a regional scale to determine the depth and extent of sedimentary basins for oil and gas exploration. To help interpret these data, the magnetic properties of rocks are measured at outcrop and digitally recorded. Modern, high-resolution aeromagnetic surveys have much improved sensitivity and can detect and map subtle features, such as magnetic contrasts between different sedimentary units.

The digital data compilation for this map includes 430 238 line-kilometres of BGS aeromagnetic data, with flight line spacings of 2 to 10 kilometres, and 206 724 line-kilometres of BGS ship-track data with a line separation of between 5 and 15 kilometres. The areas not surveyed by BGS are covered by a digital grid compiled by the Geological Survey of Canada. BGS digital magnetic data now include over 50 000 line-kilometres of new high-resolution magnetic, electromagnetic and radiometric airborne survey data covering central Britain (the *Hi-RES*-1 survey).

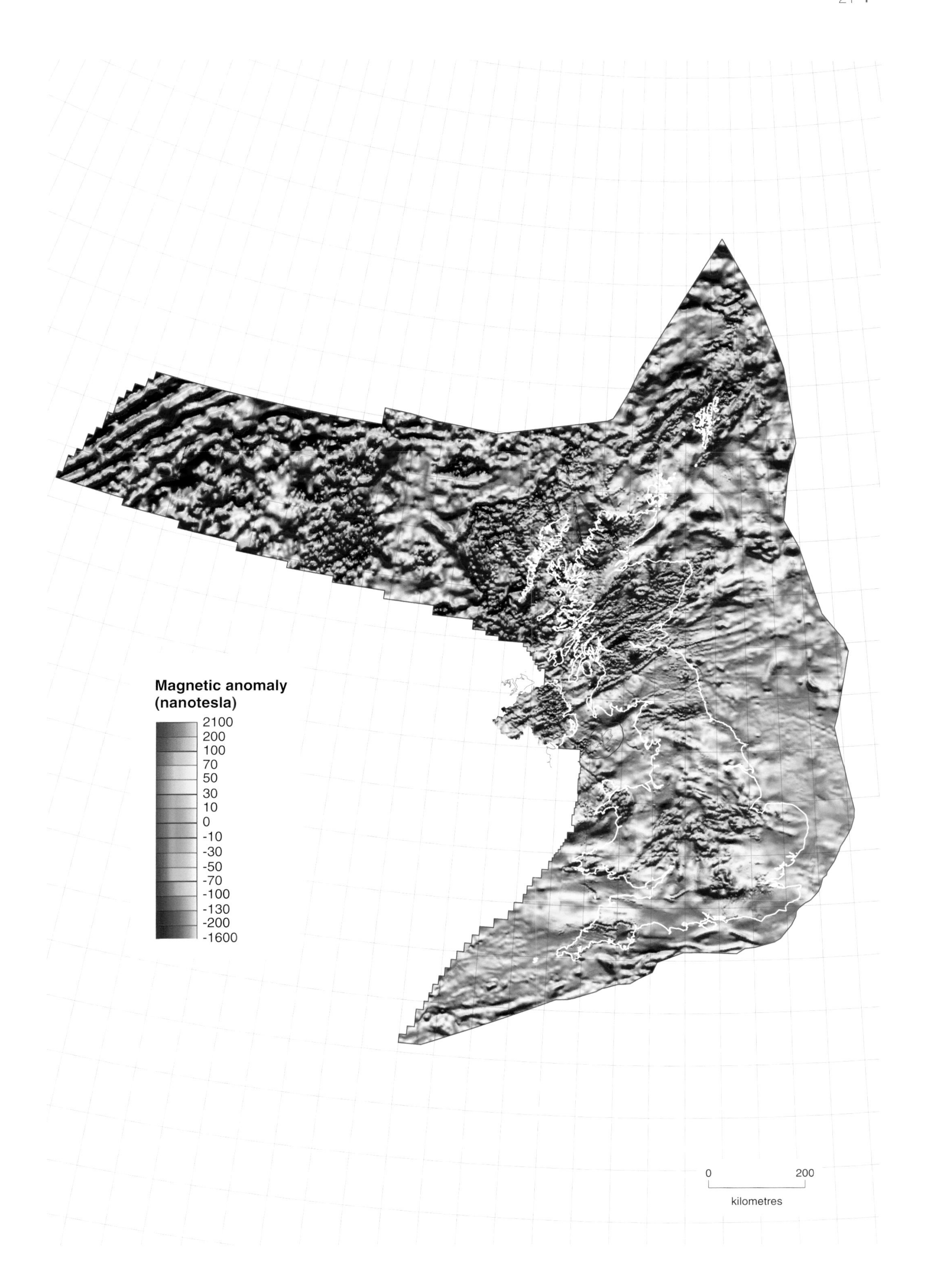
Magnetic anomaly
(nanotesla)
2100
200
100
70
50
30
10
0
-10
-30
-50
-70
-100
-130
-200
-1600
0
200
kilometres

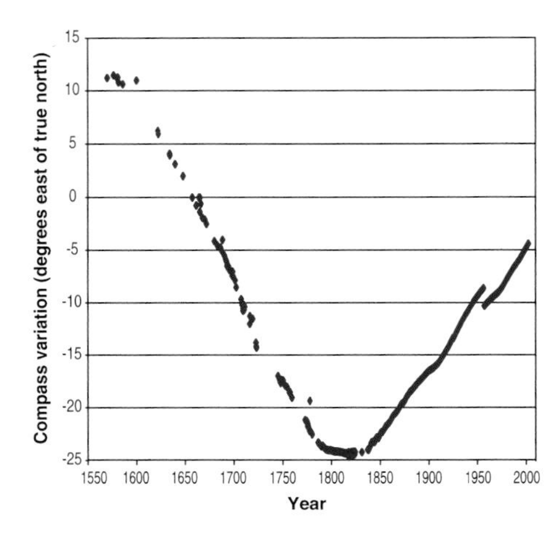

NERC©BAS, Dr John Dudeney

Base data

Compass variation

Magnetic north arrows and compass roses on maps and charts of the UK and surrounding areas are derived from magnetic field observations and models constructed by BGS. In addition to its utility for compass users, the magnetic field is used as a direction finder when drilling oil wells, where high accuracy is critical for economic reasons and to avoid intersecting older wells. BGS has worked with oil industry partners to develop methods to maximise the accuracy of the magnetic data used to guide boreholes to their targets.

The map illustrates how compass direction varied across the UK in July 2003. Magnetic north lay to the west of true north by the amount shown. The map also shows the locations of the three magnetic observatories operated by BGS, at Lerwick, Eskdalemuir and Hartland, and the positions of the 51 magnetic repeat stations used by BGS. At the observatories, absolute vector measurements of the Earth's magnetic field are made accurately and continuously, over many years, now with a time resolution of one second. Repeat stations are permanently marked sites where absolute vector observations of the Earth's magnetic field are made for a few hours every few years.

The map represents the magnetic field generated in the Earth's core. This is sufficient for most compass users, but there is a need for higher accuracy when using the magnetic field to guide the drilling of oil wells. The minute-to-minute changes in the field, especially during magnetic storms, and the effects of magnetic rocks in the Earth's crust need to taken into account. BGS has devised ways of providing site-specific near-real-time magnetic field data for drilling locations.

Data from the BGS observatories and repeat stations are central to the magnetic referencing services BGS provides to the mapping and oil industries. More information about geomagnetism and the BGS services can be found online at: *www.geomag.bgs.ac.uk*.

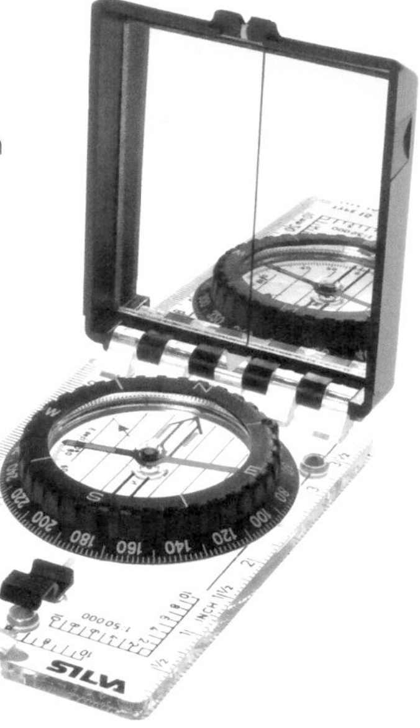

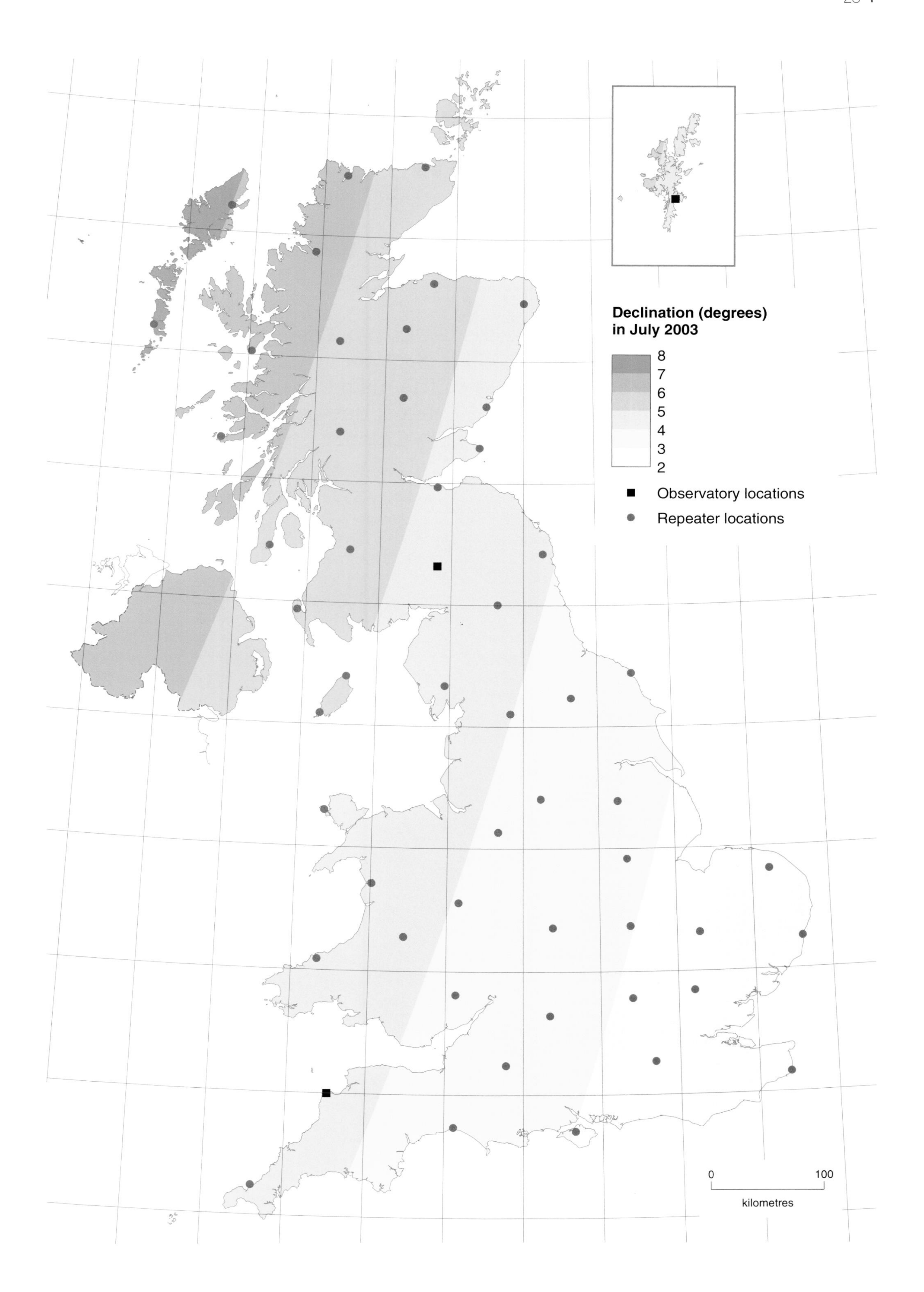
Declination (degrees) in July 2003
8
7
6
5
4
3
2
Observatory locations
Repeater locations
0
100
kilometres

Base data

Magnetic storm effects

The estimated electric field across the UK during a six-minute peak in the magnetic storm of 30th October 2003 is illustrated here. This magnetic storm was one of the largest on record. The magnetic variations were such that the compass direction changed by over 5 degrees during this six-minute period, around 21:20 GMT on 30th October.

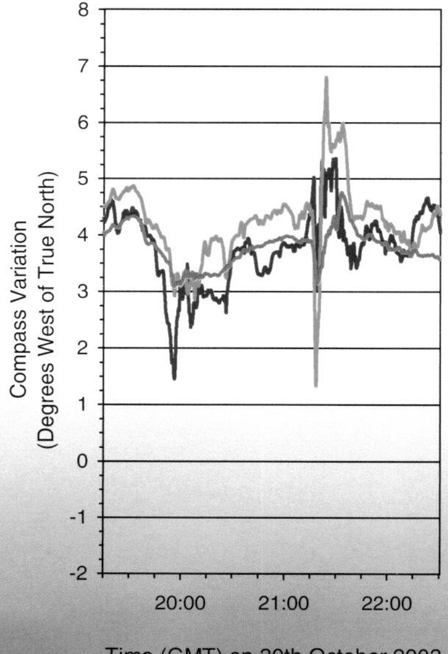

Time (GMT) on 30th October 2003

Each night from the 29th to the 31st of October 2003, there were many reports of the Aurora Borealis or Northern Lights across the UK, even from the south coast of England. The magnetic storm associated with this display had been predicted by BGS scientists. It was the result of a series of major solar eruptions, known as coronal mass ejections. The rapidly varying geomagnetic field induced an electric field in the Earth.

Knowledge of the surface electric field enables us to estimate the magnitude and direction of induced electrical currents driven through any large-scale conducting structure, such as the UK power grid and networks of oil and gas pipelines. These geomagnetically induced currents can damage unprotected electrically conducting equipment, as demonstrated by the collapse of the Canadian Hydro-Quebec power grid during the great magnetic storm of 13th March 1989. Understanding the risk helps power companies and others in the UK to protect their equipment and maintain system integrity.

The surface electric field shown on the map is estimated directly from rapid geomagnetic variations measured at the three UK magnetic observatories operated by BGS, and the electric field is calculated on a 10 kilometre grid. The electric field model takes into account the three-dimensional terrain structure and conductivity of the UK and its continental shelf, as well as the conductivity and depth of the surrounding sea and the Atlantic Ocean. The data for this model were derived from BGS and University of Edinburgh sources.

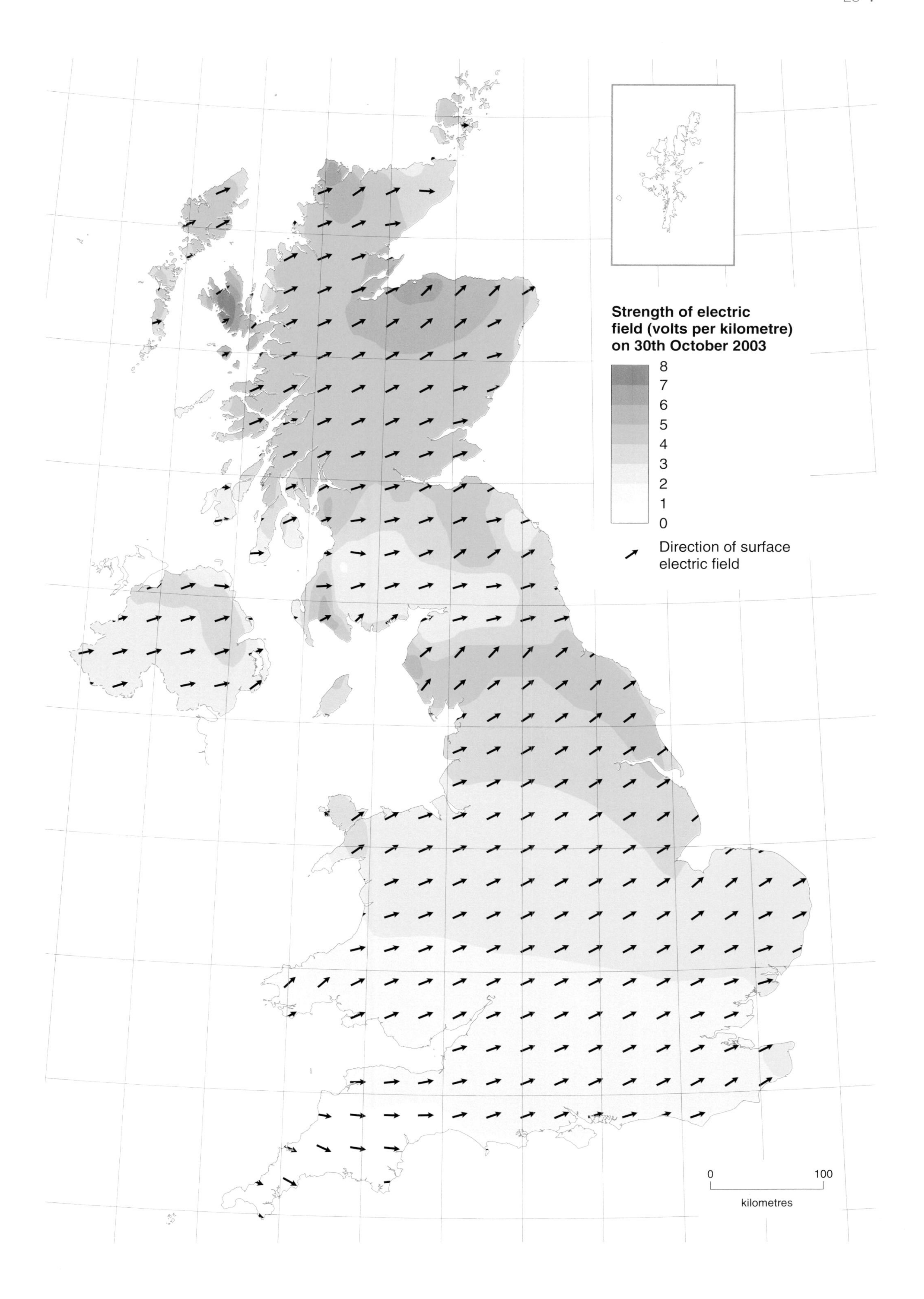

Strength of electric field (volts per kilometre) on 30th October 2003
8
7
6
5
4
3
2
1
0
Direction of surface electric field
0
100
kilometres

Base data

Historical geology

The *Geological Survey* was founded in 1835 when Henry de la Beche was commissioned to produce the geology maps of Devon. In the years that followed a large archive has been assembled, and BGS is now the custodian of a vast and diverse collection of maps, notebooks, photographs and records. This unique collection is of considerable scientific and historical value. It includes originals of William Smith's maps of 1815 and 1820, and early maps of Scotland by L A Necker (1808) and J MacCulloch (1834), a complete collection of the *County Series* six-inch geological maps, hand-illustrated field notebooks of early geological surveyors and a photographic collection that contains some of the earliest geological field photographs.

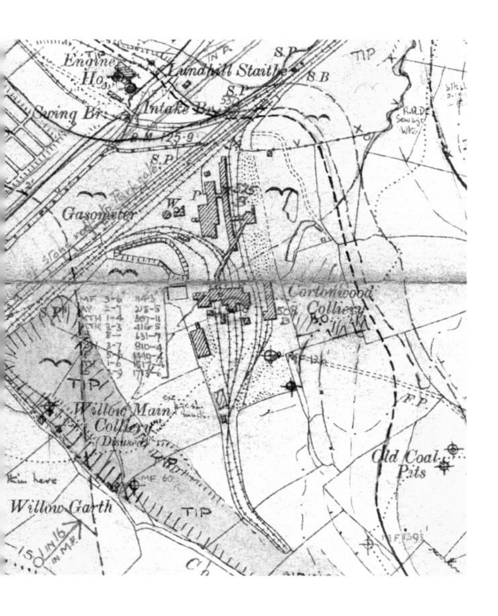

The map opposite is a copy of William Smith's map of 1815. The map, originally produced at a scale of about 1:950 400, has been digitised and reduced. Smith's work is described in recent books by Simon Winchester and Hugh Torrence. His maps, which are now regarded as things of antiquity and beauty, were a very practical contribution to the mineral exploration and hence to the industrial development of Britain. They also set a pattern for geological maps that was used in many other countries.

While much of the archival material held by BGS is of historical value, many of the items have a very real and practical application today. For example, the old six-inch *County Series* maps record features that are no longer apparent. Urbanisation and modern agriculture have obscured many of the old mine shafts, quarries, water wells and industrial sites. The maps and the accompanying notebooks and photographs of the early surveyors describe features that have long since disappeared from view, but some of these have left a legacy that is still relevant today, for example old mine workings, or sites that have been polluted by industrial or mining processes.

BGS is progressively converting this archive into digital (raster) form. The first priority is to ensure that back-up copies of the documents are secure and available, but having them in digital form also means that BGS can disseminate copies more easily to a wider audience. Borehole logs, geological maps (including the complete collection of the six-inch *County Series* 'Standards' and 'field slips') and selected photographs are the first to be digitised; other documents will follow as resources allow.

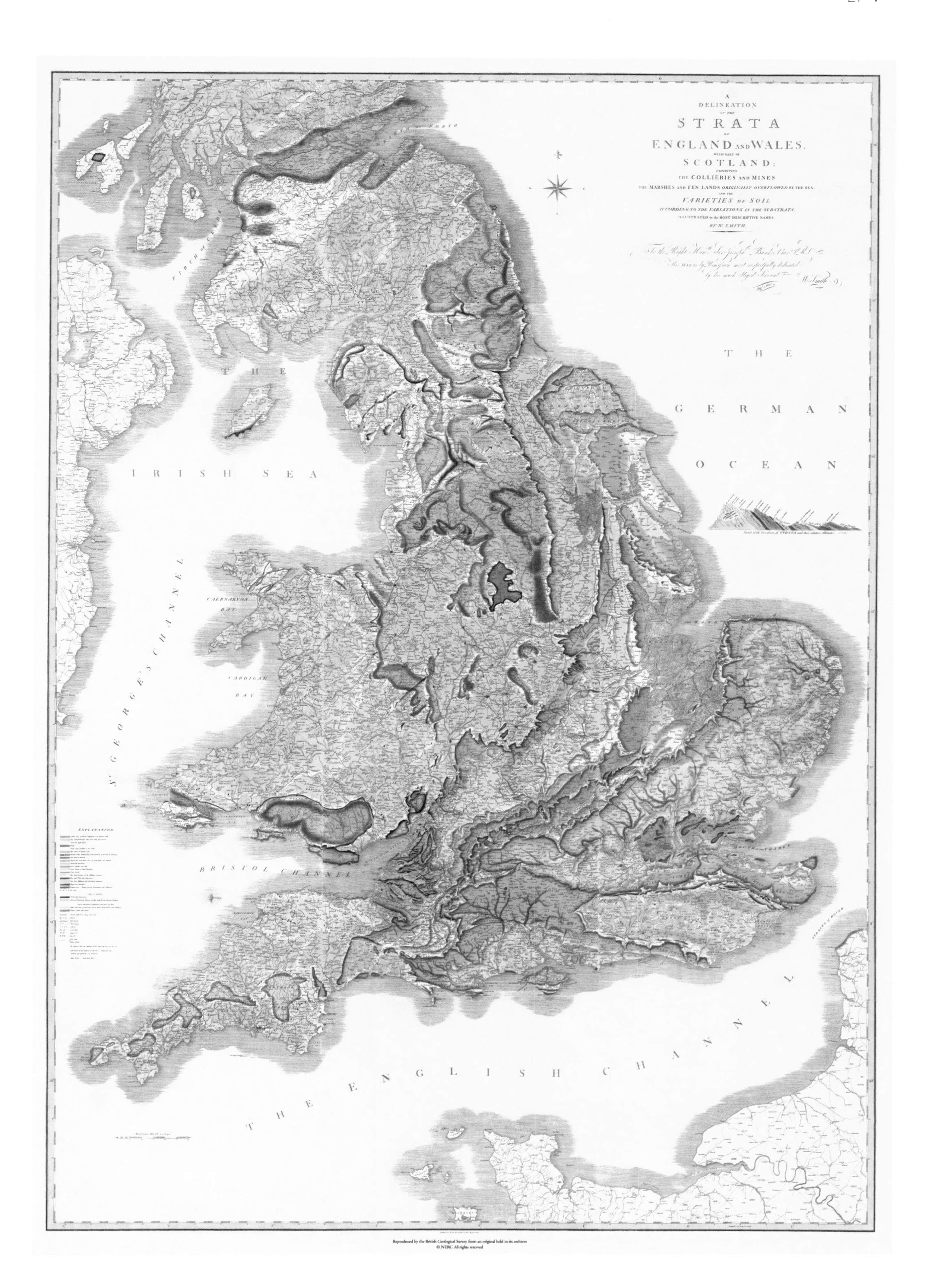

A DELINEATION OF THE STRATA OF ENGLAND AND WALES, WITH PART OF SCOTLAND;
EXHIBITING THE COLLIERIES AND MINES
THE MARSHES AND FEN LANDS ORIGINALLY OVERFLOWED BY THE SEA,
AND THE VARIETIES OF SOIL
ACCORDING TO THE VARIATIONS IN THE SUBSTRATA.
ILLUSTRATED by the MOST DESCRIPTIVE NAMES
BY W. SMITH.
THE GERMAN OCEAN
IRISH SEA
CAERNARVON BAY
CARDIGAN BAY
ST. GEORGE'S CHANNEL
BRISTOL CHANNEL
EXPLANATION
THE ENGLISH CHANNEL

River Caerfanell, Blaen Y Glyn, Brecon Beacons. Graham Bell, BGS © NERC

Britain beneath our feet

Land quality and groundwater

Geology and geochemistry both play a significant role in defining the quality of land and water. The *G-BASE* programme *(Geochemical Baseline Survey of the Environment)* is a long-term strategic geochemical survey of the UK, which started in 1969 and now covers 80 per cent of the country. Britain is fortunate in possessing extensive subsurface water resources. But groundwater is not only a resource, it also provides a significant pathway for pollution.

The chemical composition of the surface of the UK is being mapped by sampling and analyses of stream sediment, stream water and soil.

Five examples of the emerging results of the *G-BASE* programme are presented here. Over 190 000 samples have been collected and analysed for up to 55 elements. *G-BASE* provides a baseline dataset that can be used to evaluate the variation of chemical elements in our environment, and helps to assess the risk to human health from contaminated land.

Groundwater is a major source of supply for many people in the south and east of the country. The resource is often under threat from excessive pumping and, increasingly, from industrial and agricultural pollution.

Modern geological mapping helps to define land and water quality. Since the mid-1960s, BGS has routinely mapped artificial (anthropogenic) deposits and features as part of the 1:10 000 scale geological survey programme. Thus, open and infilled quarries, waste tips and spoil heaps, major earthworks and many other features have been delineated and recorded, and this information is now available in digital format (see page 6, Surface Geology).

Aluminium
Antimony
Arsenic
Barium
Beryllium
Bismuth
Boron
Bromine
Calcium
Cadmium
Cerium
Cesium
Chlorine
Cobalt
Chromium
Copper
Fluorine
Gallium
Germanium
Hafnium
Holmium
Iodine
Iron
Lanthanum
Lead
Lithium
Magnesium
Manganese
Molybdenum
Neodymium
Nickel
Niobium
Nitrogen
Phosphorus
Potassium
Rubidium
Samarium
Silver
Scandium
Selenium
Silicon
Sodium
Strontium
Tantalum
Tellurium
Thallium
Thorium
Tin
Titanium
Tungsten
Uranium
Vanadium
Yttrium
Zinc
Zirconium

Land quality and groundwater

Hydrogeology

Hydrogeological maps provide the starting point for an understanding of the role groundwater plays in the environment. While water is present underground almost anywhere that you might look in Britain, its behaviour depends on the specific geological conditions. Hydrogeological maps focus on aquifers; these are rocks through which water can flow easily. The more easily water will flow through the rock the more productive the aquifer, and thus more water can be abstracted or will flow from the rocks into rivers.

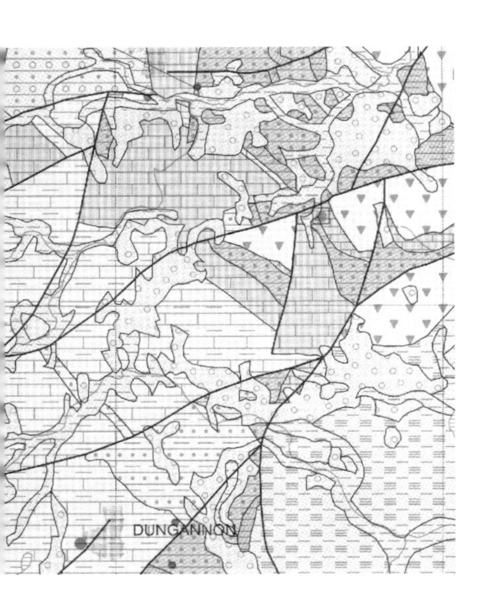

In some rocks, such as sandstone, water will flow though the pore space in between grains of sand; in others, such as chalk, most of the flow will take place through fractures and fissures. The difference can be important as water travels quicker through fissures than it does through the pores of a rock. This can affect how pollution travels though an aquifer, how quickly the aquifer will respond to rainfall, and how much water can be abstracted by wells or boreholes. Rocks that allow only very slow water flow underlie some areas. While there may not be enough groundwater in these areas to provide large supplies of water for human use, the water that is present may still play an important role in the local ecology by supporting streams and wetlands.

Hydrogeological maps are produced by combining digital geological map data with information on how each rock type interacts with groundwater. This information comes from a comprehensive inventory and database of wells and water boreholes, including data on water levels and flow rates. BGS holds data on over 105 000 water wells and boreholes in its *WellMaster* database. These can be combined with digital geological map data to produce hydrogeological maps at a range of scales, including data on water quality and the exploitation of water resources as well as information on aquifer productivity.

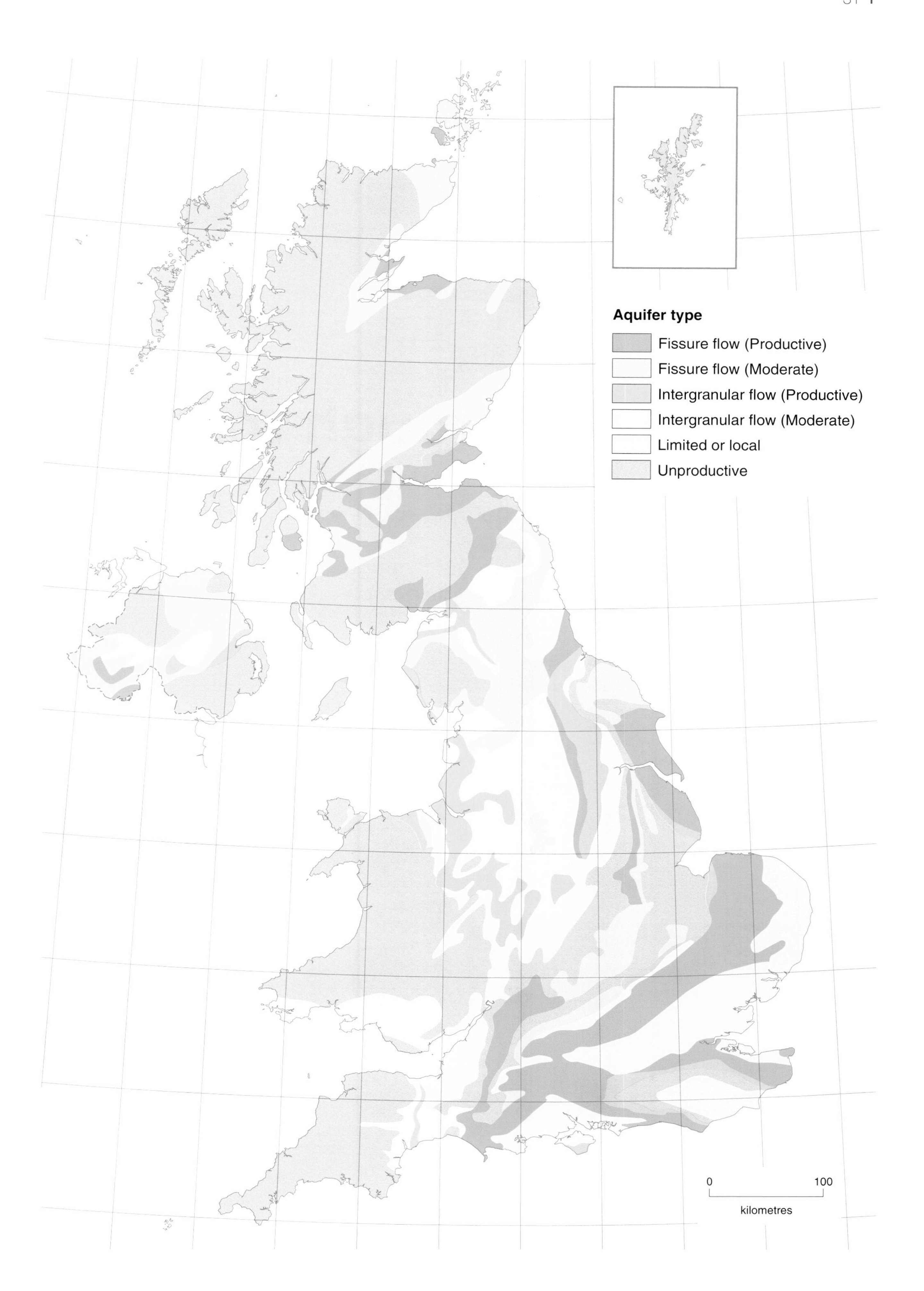

Aquifer type
Fissure flow (Productive)
Fissure flow (Moderate)
Intergranular flow (Productive)
Intergranular flow (Moderate)
Limited or local
Unproductive
0
100
kilometres

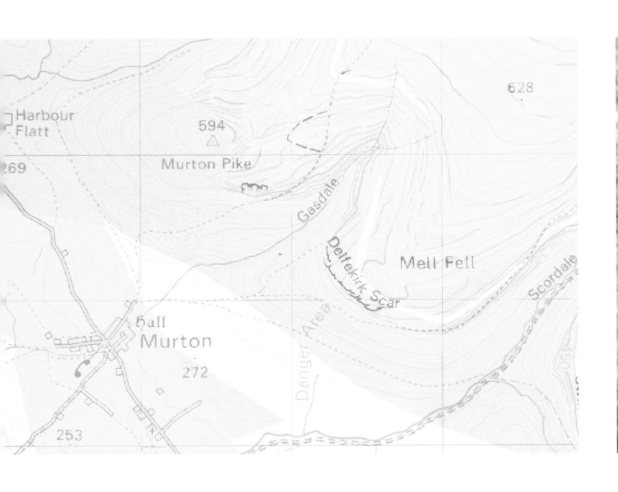

Land quality and groundwater

Water flow through rocks

This dataset gives an assessment of how easily water can flow through a rock formation, but with no assessment of the quantity of water that is actually present. This contrasts with the hydrogeological map that focuses on aquifers — rock formations that contain economically useful quantities of groundwater.

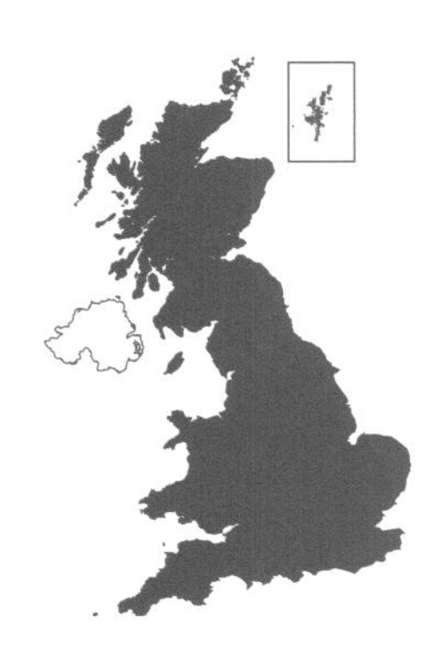

Each rock has a characteristic set of properties that will affect how easily water flows through it. The properties include the size and shape of individual grains that make up the rock (e.g. sandstone), and the extent of fracturing in harder rocks (e.g. limestone and granite). Unfortunately, these properties are quite variable even within one rock type, so a range of values have been assigned.

This map shows the higher range of values.The ease with which water flows through a rock can be critical. In rocks where water flows easily, pollution incidents can quickly affect water supplies and rivers, but where flow is slower there is more opportunity for any pollution to be dispersed and reduced naturally. Rocks through which water flows easily are likely to allow ready recharge of their aquifers, and they provide better prospects for the drilling of wells and boreholes to provide water for drinking, agriculture or industry.

Assessment of water flow is based on integrating digital geological map data with point measurements made on individual rock samples and the results of field tests of water flow made on wells and boreholes.

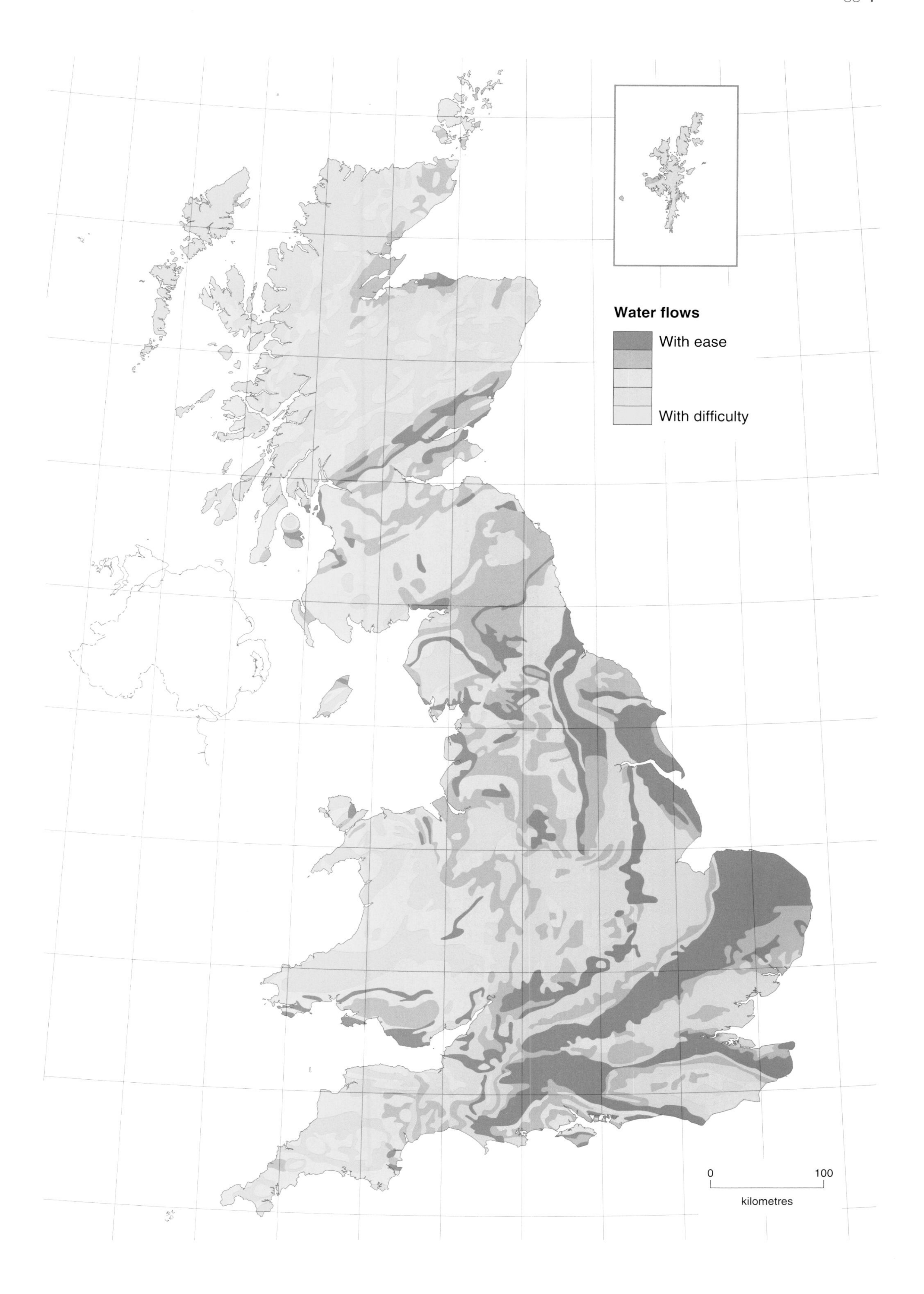
Water flows
With ease
With difficulty
0
100
kilometres

Land quality and groundwater

Groundwater signature

Hydrogeologists can assess the origin of groundwater by measuring its ratio of naturally occurring, stable, non-radioactive isotopes. And because these ratios are preserved in the bones of animals and humans that drink the water they can be used in archaeological and forensic investigations.

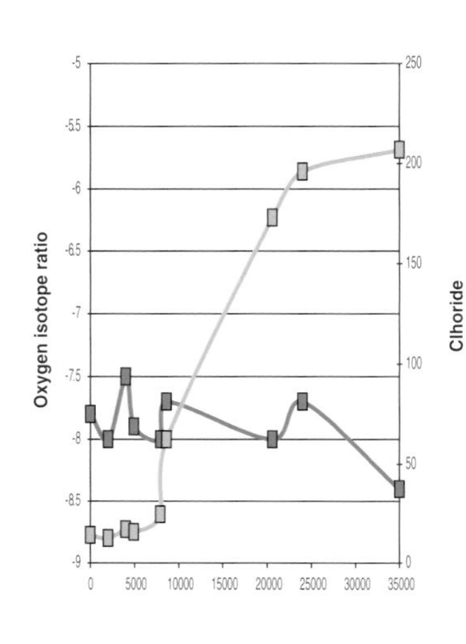

The speed of water flow in rocks is normally very slow, giving plenty of time for the water to be changed chemically by reactions with the minerals in the rocks — the process that gives mineral water a distinct flavour. However, while groundwater changes chemically, the ratio of natural isotopes of particular elements, such as hydrogen and oxygen, in the water tends to be fixed from the moment it reaches the water table and remains unchanged as it flows through the rocks. The map shows the variation in an isotope of oxygen, which is concentrated in rainfall as prevailing winds cross the country from the south-west.

These isotopic *signatures* can be used in many ways. Geoscientists and hydrologists use them to investigate how water recharges aquifers; engineers can use the ratios to distinguish between natural groundwater and leakage from pipes and sewers; archaeologists have used the ratios to study patterns of migration in prehistoric man, and forensic scientists use the data to help identify the origin of unidentified bodies and bones.

The data on the map represent a generalisation of a unique database of groundwater compiled by BGS, which includes data on natural oxygen and hydrogen isotopes, as well as other elements and chemicals that can be used to trace groundwater origins. The data are available as maps and detailed point analyses.

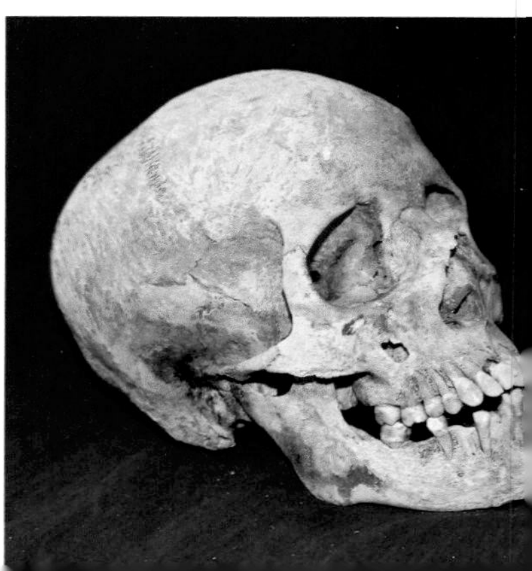

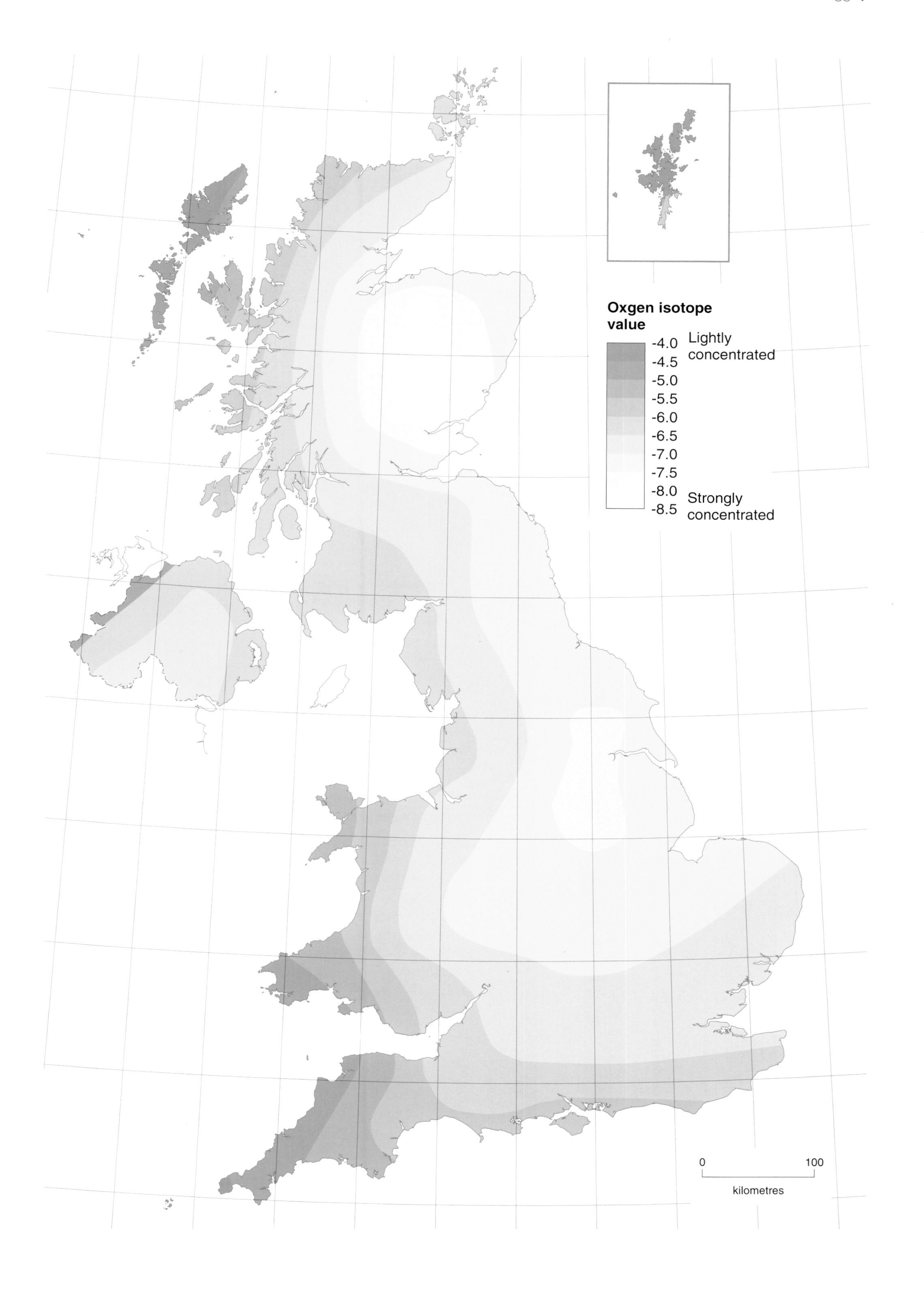
Oxgen isotope value
-4.0
-4.5
-5.0
-5.5
-6.0
-6.5
-7.0
-7.5
-8.0
-8.5
Lightly concentrated
Strongly concentrated
0
100
kilometres

Land quality and groundwater

Groundwater level

This map shows the generalised height of the surface of the water table across England and Wales. When combined with digital elevation models, the data can be used to assess the probable depth to groundwater at a given point. At a regional scale, groundwater levels fluctuate seasonally in response to changes in rainfall. Over the longer term, levels vary in response to abstraction, changes in land use and climate.

A national monitoring network reviews groundwater levels in key water wells and boreholes in order to assess seasonal changes and their impact on water resources. This also provides a baseline for climate change studies. Locally, levels of groundwater can be strongly affected by interaction with rivers and lakes, and by the effect of pumping from wells and water boreholes.

The groundwater level is important in a number of ways. It influences the cost of exploiting groundwater resources, not just conventional use for water supply, but also for new technologies such as heat pumps that use the geothermal energy stored in groundwater to heat homes and offices. Although deeper groundwater is more expensive to exploit, it may also be better protected from pollution, as infiltrating rainfall will have taken longer to reach the water table and pollution may have been reduced by interactions between the water and the rocks it has travelled through.

The data illustrated by the map opposite come from a number of sources, including information held in the BGS *WellMaster* database and the *National Groundwater Level Archive*, which includes data stretching back to the 19th century. These measurements were made by BGS, the Environment Agency, the Scottish Environmental Protection Agency and their predecessors. They are derived from more than 2000 boreholes. Also included are interpreted contour data from 1:625 000 and 1:50 000 scale maps.

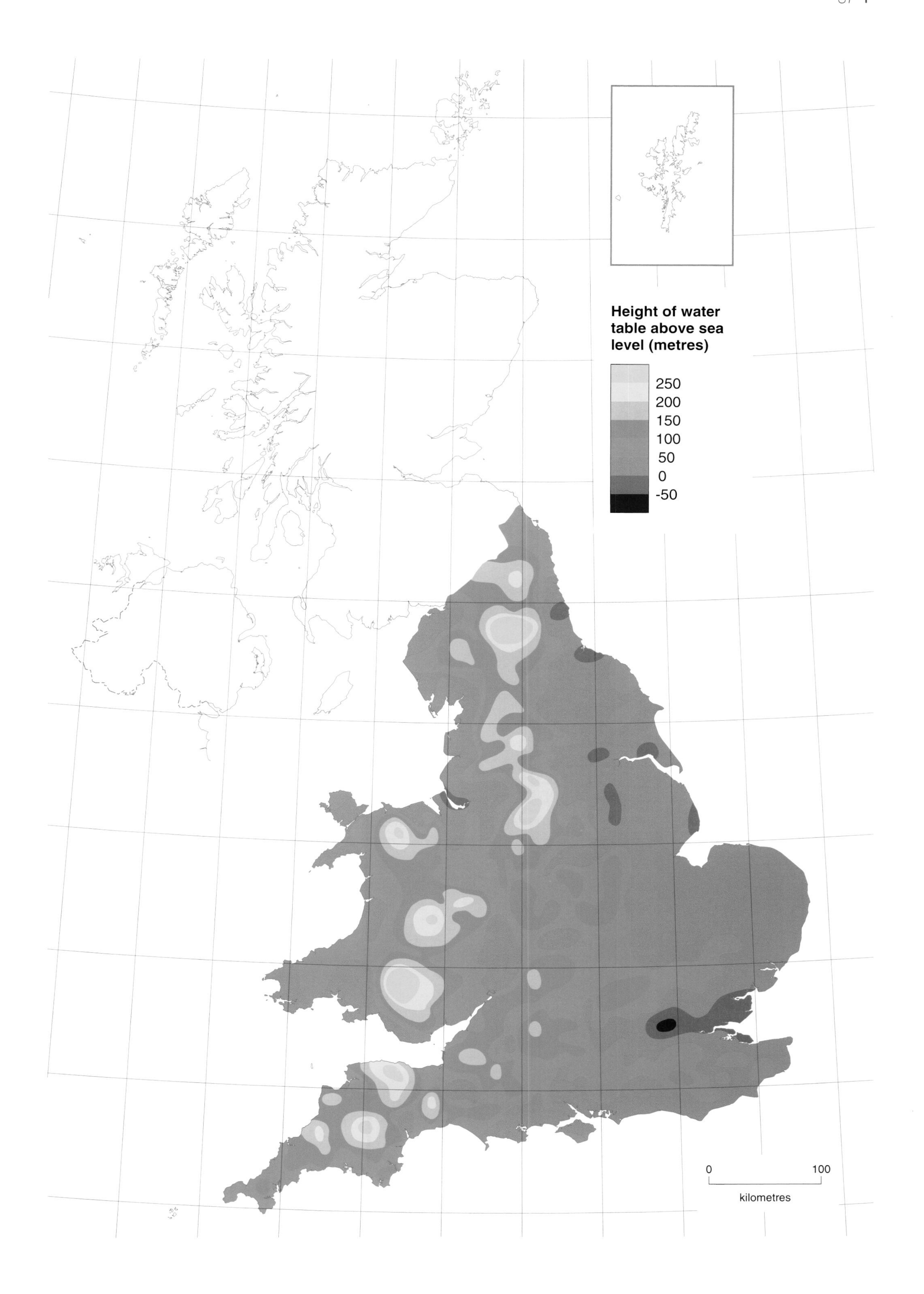
Height of water table above sea level (metres)
250
200
150
100
50
0
-50
0
100
kilometres

Land quality and groundwater

Groundwater vulnerability

This map illustrates a dataset that evaluates groundwater vulnerability. A detailed version was prepared for the Scottish Environmental Protection Agency to assist in the introduction of new legislation that will improve the management of Scottish groundwater resources. This generalised version of the map highlights environmentally vulnerable upland areas where there is little natural groundwater, but where the water present is easily polluted.

This particular dataset concentrates on environmental issues. The data can also be combined with information about aquifers used for water supply so that sensitive areas can be identified and protected from polluting activities. For example, chemical processing or landfill sites should not be sited where they create a risk to the water supply and environment. With the addition of data on land use, derivative maps have been prepared to show where the use of nitrate fertilizer may contaminate aquifers.

Groundwater vulnerability maps may be prepared using different methodologies. Source information can include water level, digital geological map data (in particular thickness of superficial deposits), soil type, aquifer productivity and chemical analyses of water from boreholes, wells and springs.

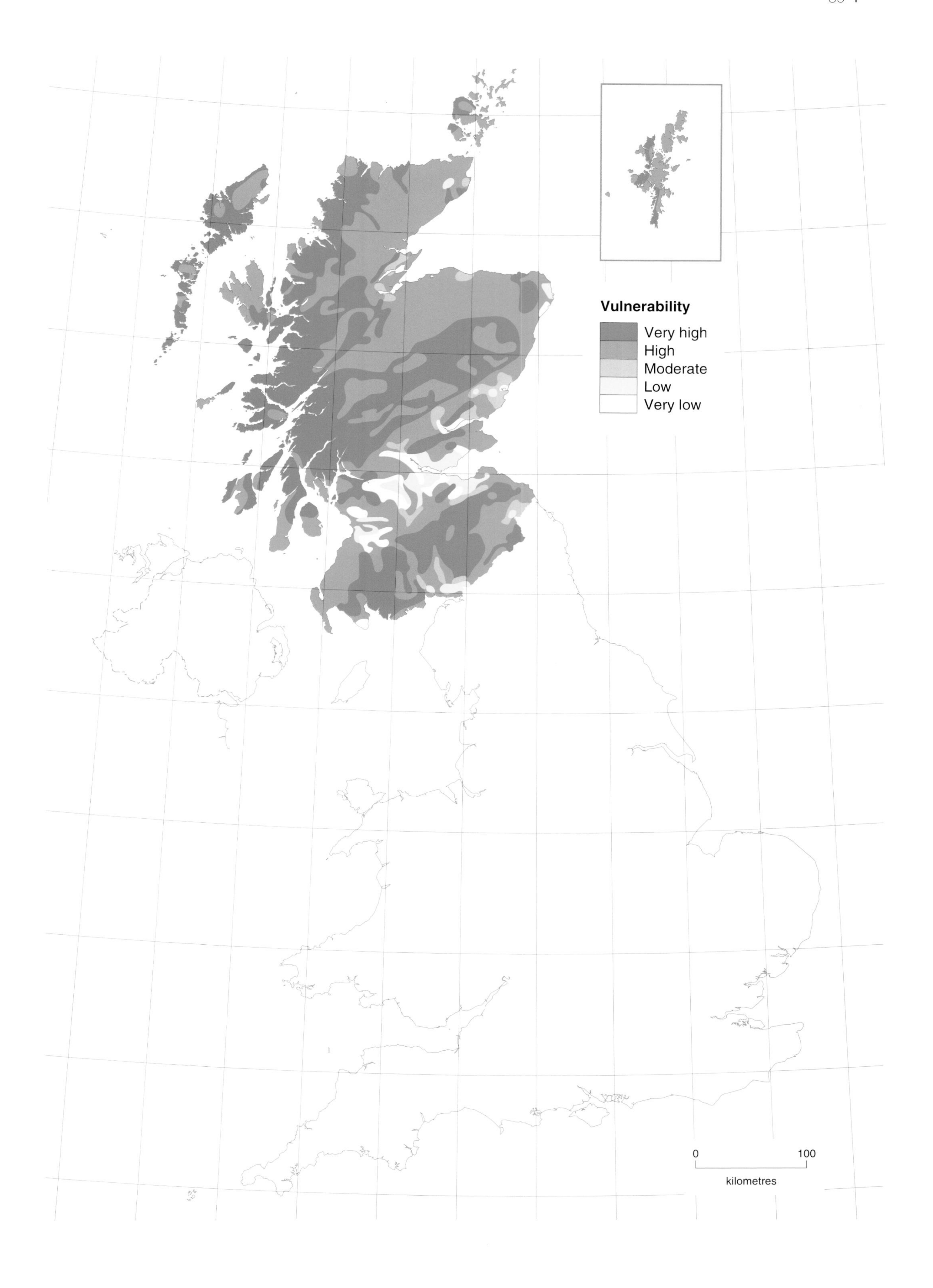
Vulnerability
Very high
High
Moderate
Low
Very low
0
100
kilometres

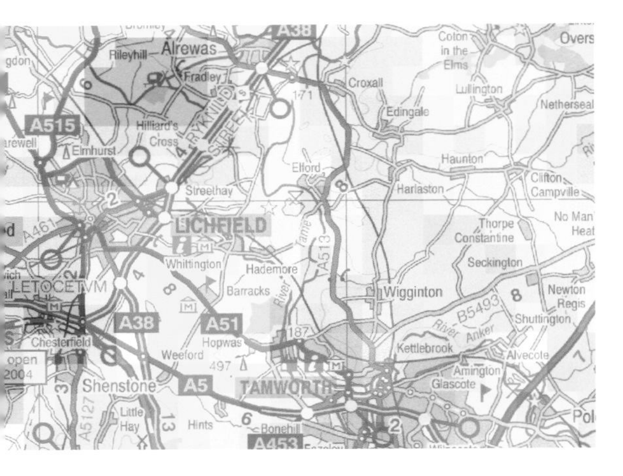

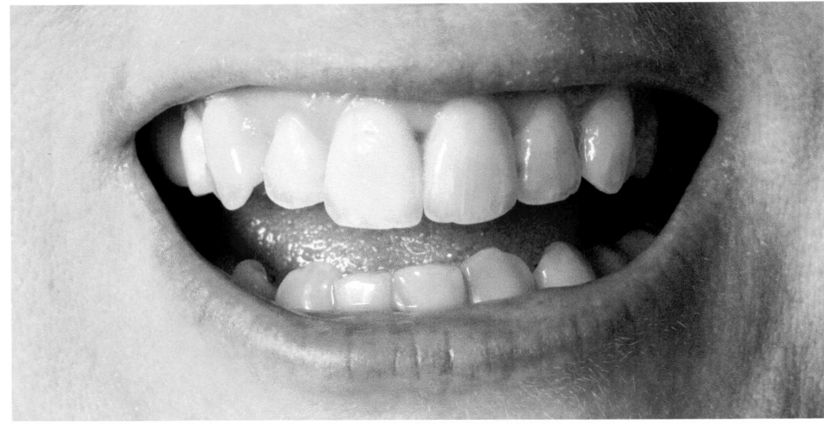

Land quality and groundwater

Fluoride in stream water

The total concentration of fluoride in stream water shows a general increase from west to east throughout much of the UK. Statistical analyses of the data suggest this is due to variation in annual rainfall, which decreases from west to east, and the nature of the bedrock.

Higher annual rainfall leads to greater dilution of the fluoride derived from water-rock interaction. In addition, the amount of fluoride supplied from both bedrock and superficial deposits varies considerably, resulting in a complex spatial pattern.

Where surface water resources are used to supply drinking water, data on fluoride concentration can be used to determine the natural fluoride content, and thus can contribute to the long-running national debate surrounding fluoridation of water.

The map opposite is a very generalised image. However, the data from which it is derived comprise detailed analyses of about 30 000 individual samples taken from streams across the country. These data were collected as part of the on-going *G-BASE* survey. The data are in digital format and can be made available as data files and in map form.

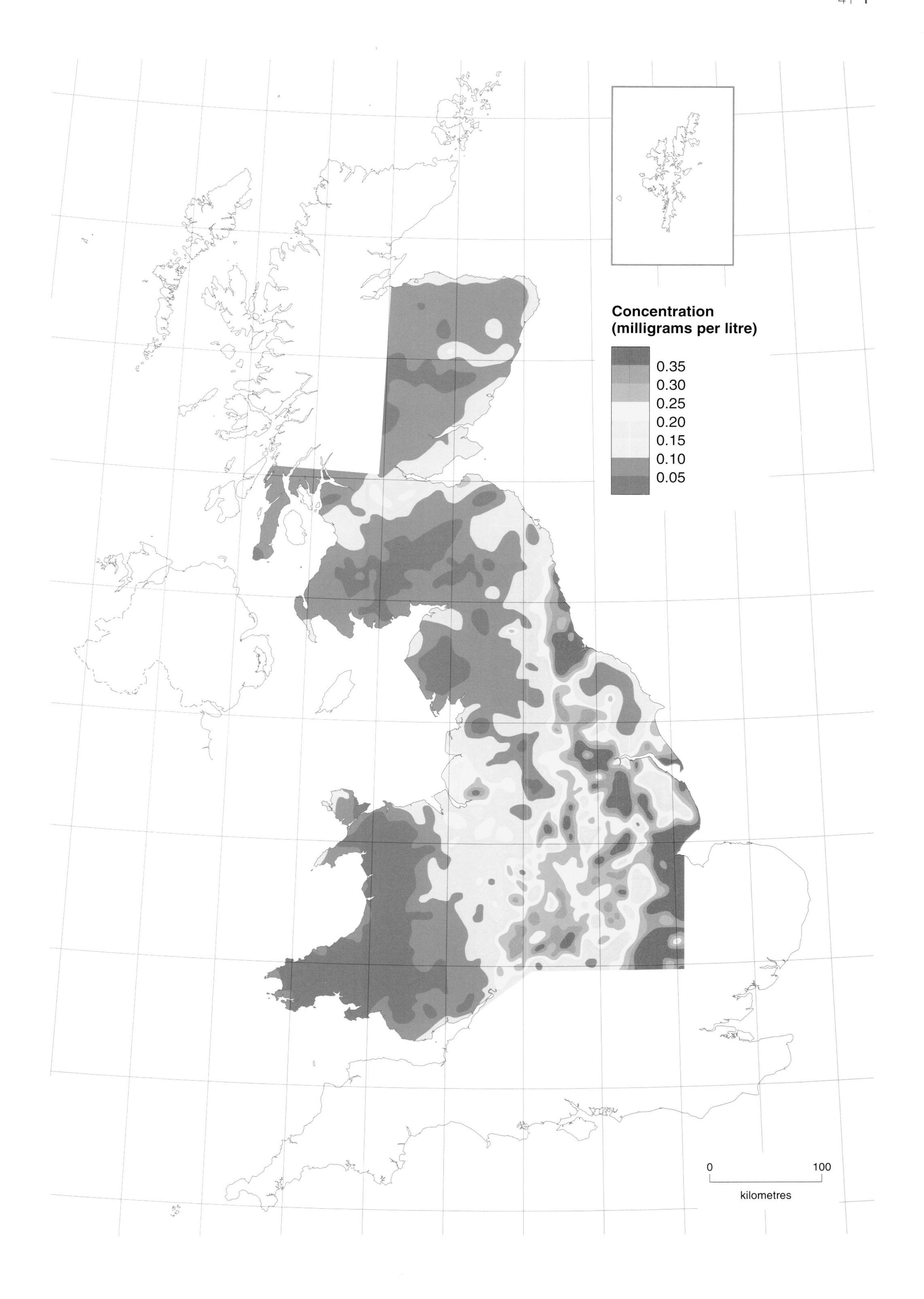
Concentration
(milligrams per litre)
0.35
0.30
0.25
0.20
0.15
0.10
0.05
0
100
kilometres

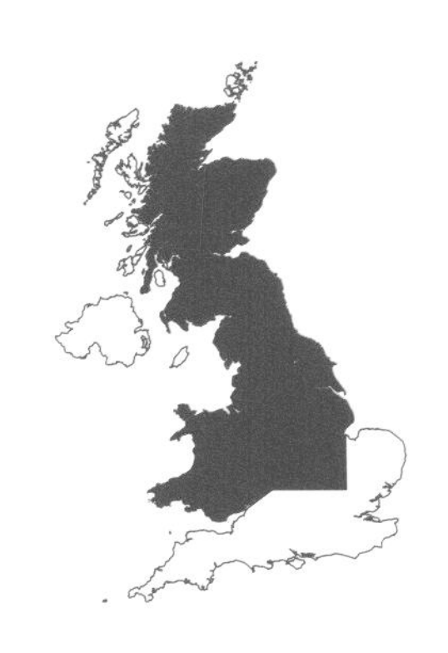

Land quality and groundwater

Stream water acidity (pH)

This map shows the distribution of stream water acidity throughout much of Britain. With the exception of some areas in southern Scotland and northern England, there is a general decline in stream water acidity from the north-west to the south-east of Britain.

The two dominant controls on the distribution of acidity are variations in annual rainfall and the chemical composition of bedrock. Farther west, where on average there is more rainfall and the rock tends to be less permeable, there is less opportunity for water-rock interaction, which helps to reduce the natural acidity in rainfall and that derived from the soil.

Although there is currently less concern regarding the impact of acid deposition in the UK (commonly referred to as acid rain) than during the 1990s, high-resolution data on the distribution of stream water acidity can be helpful in highlighting areas most sensitive to surface water acidification.

This generalised map is based on the analysis of around 52 000 individual samples collected between 1970 and 2003 (during the summer months). The source data were collected as part of the BGS *G-BASE* programme. The data are available in digital format as data files or as customised digital maps.

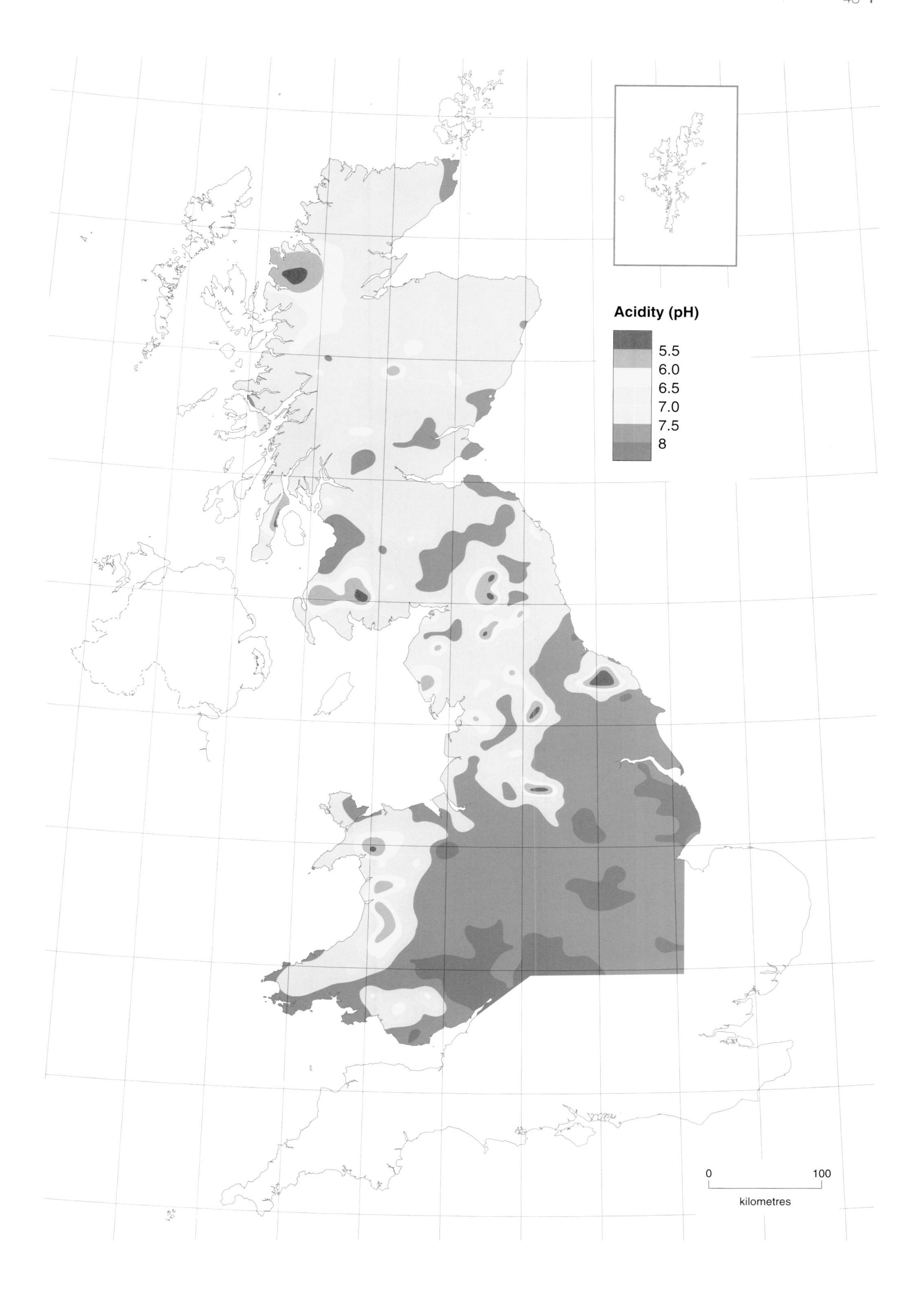
Acidity (pH)
5.5
6.0
6.5
7.0
7.5
8
0
100
kilometres

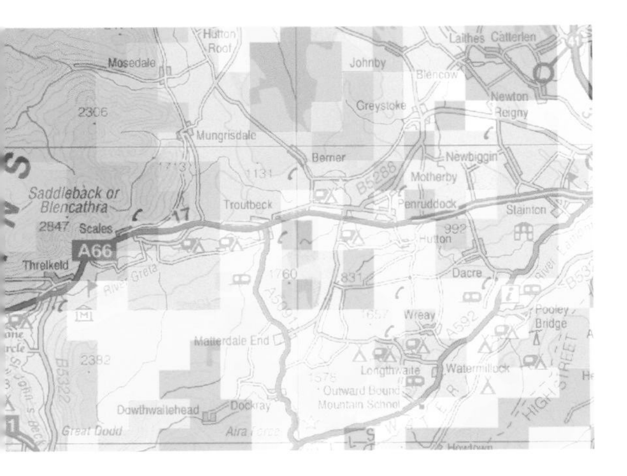

Land quality and groundwater

Copper in stream sediment

This map, and the succeeding pages showing uranium levels, illustrate the distribution of just two of the elements that BGS has analysed in UK stream sediments as part of the on-going *G-BASE* programme. In general, it is the composition of the bedrock geology and any overlying superficial deposits that controls the chemical elements in stream sediments. But other factors, including human activities, such as mining, urbanisation and waste disposal, can have a considerable impact too.

Copper levels are naturally high over the volcanic rocks of Skye and Mull. Mining areas in the Lake District and north Wales show up clearly on the map, as do the high levels around urban conurbations. The low copper levels evident over most of the Scottish highlands pose a potential problem for agriculture.

The *G-BASE* data also include stream water and soil analyses. The data allow us to establish the mobility and toxicity of the chemical elements in our environment, which is critical in identifying contamination and pollution.

Stream sediment samples have been collected across the UK at a density of about one sample per 1.5 square kilometres. Up to 48 elements have been analysed in each sample, and more than five million element determinations are held in the digital database.

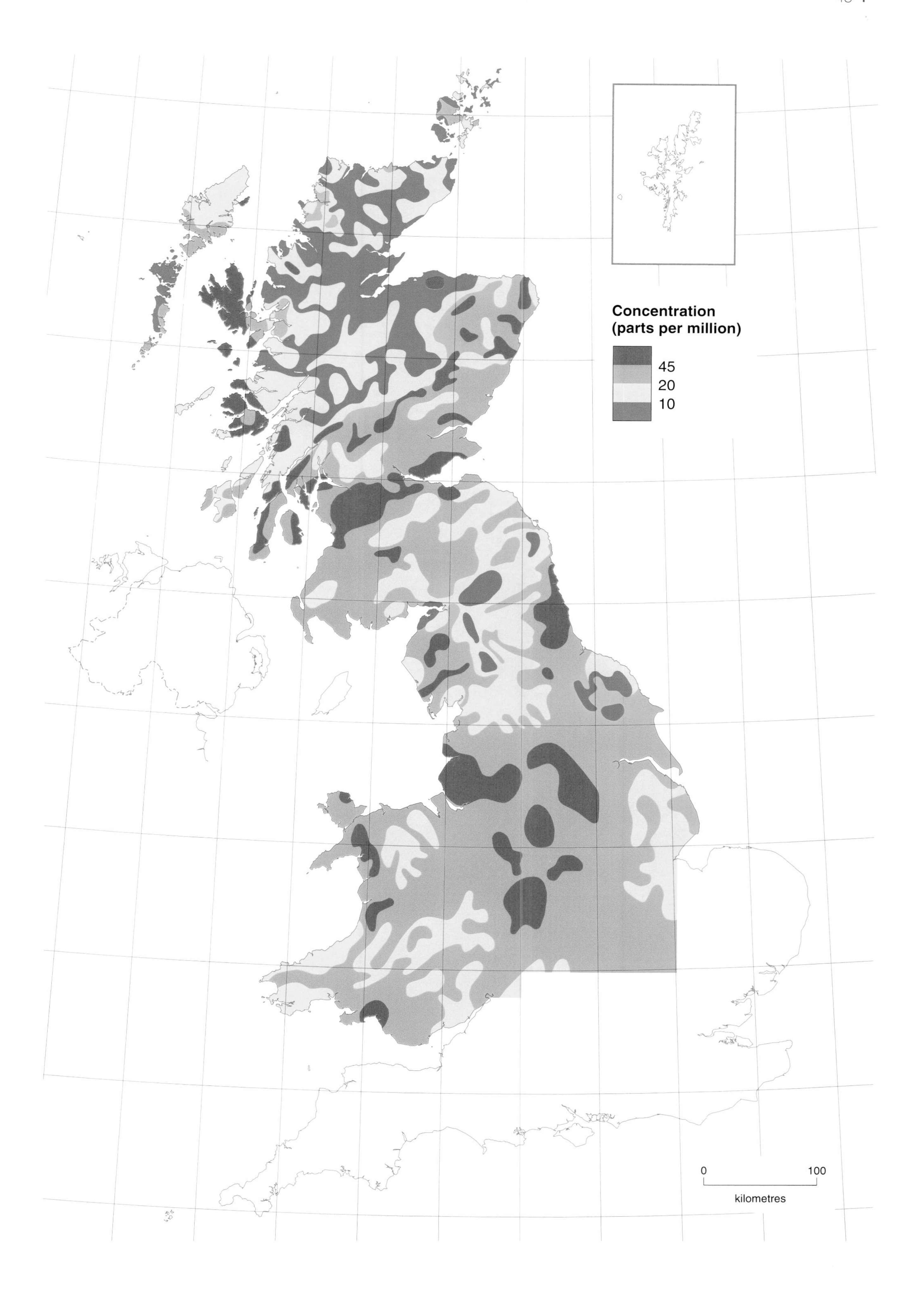
Concentration
(parts per million)
45
20
10
0
100
kilometres

Land quality and groundwater

Uranium in stream sediment

Uranium is one of the elements that has been assessed as part of the *G-BASE* programme. The distribution of this element in stream sediments is controlled by the underlying bedrock geology. High levels of uranium are linked to the outcrop of granite, for example in Scotland and northern England.

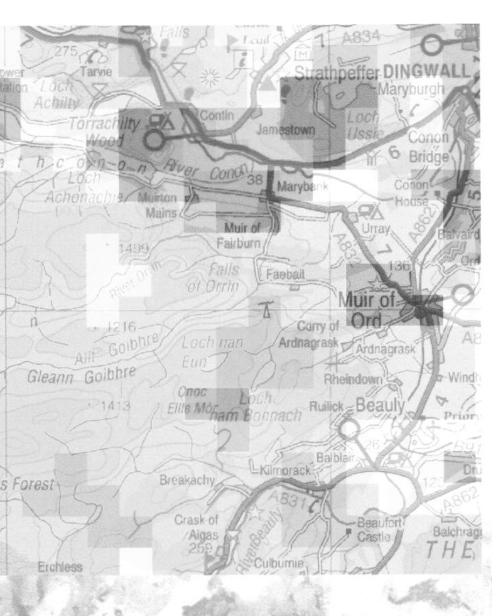

Higher levels of uranium are also associated with black shales of the Carboniferous rocks of Derbyshire, Lancashire and Yorkshire. Low levels occur in parts of Wales, the south Midlands and the Hebrides.

Together with other *G-BASE* data from stream waters and soil analyses, stream sediment data provide the base-line information that is required to assess the variation in chemicals in our environment, their mobility and toxicity.

The database currently contains over five million element determinations; several thousand more are added annually as the survey progresses across the UK. Samples are collected at a density of about one per 1.5 square kilometres. The normalised data are available digitally, as either tabular information or in map format.

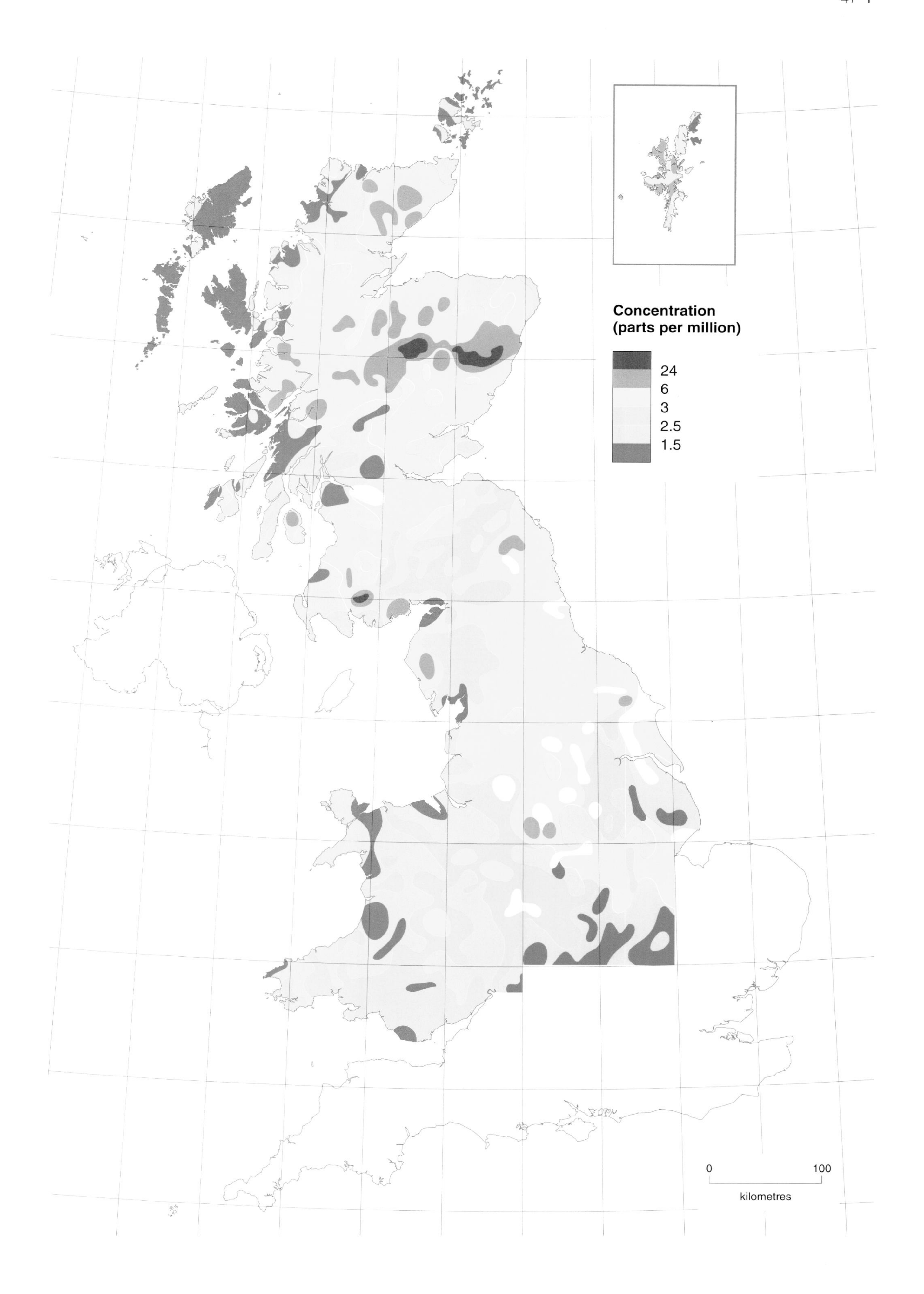
Concentration
(parts per million)
24
6
3
2.5
1.5
0
100
kilometres

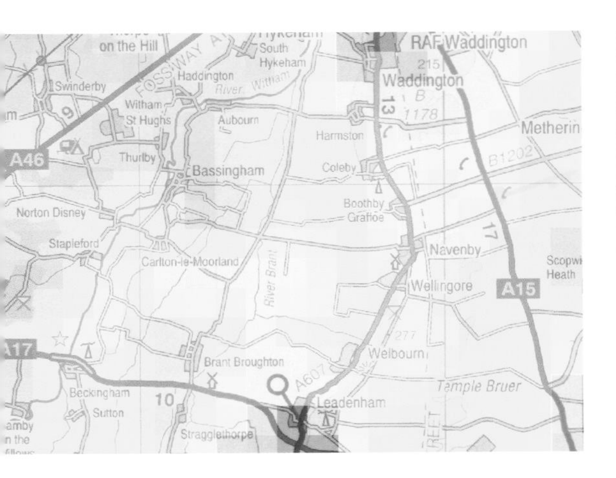

Land quality and groundwater

Arsenic in soil

The concentration of arsenic has been sampled by BGS from approximately 28 000 individual soil sites in England. The mineral content and chemical composition of soils largely reflects the weathering of the underlying parent material — either the bedrock geology or the unconsolidated superficial deposits. This can be seen in the distribution of arsenic concentration on the map.

In central and eastern England, a high arsenic concentration occurs in soils derived from the Jurassic and Cretaceous rocks. However, in south-west England, the highest arsenic concentrations are associated with mineral deposits and associated mine waste that has resulted from their exploitation.

Due to the toxic properties of certain chemical elements that include arsenic, the UK Government has established Soil Guideline Values (SGV) for a range of substances in order to aid the assessment of risk to human health from land contamination. The SGV for arsenic in residential areas and allotments is 20 mg kg^{-1}. This does not imply that soil with arsenic concentrations above this threshold poses a significant risk to human health. However, it does indicate that where this limit is exceeded further work is needed to assess the potential for harm. This map shows that across significant areas of England the concentration of arsenic in the soil is above this threshold. By reviewing this geochemical data in conjunction with geological and other information, BGS can help local authorities and consultants to establish whether the arsenic is likely to be of natural origin.

The data are available in tabular format or as a map. Sampling of the southern England region is currently in progress.

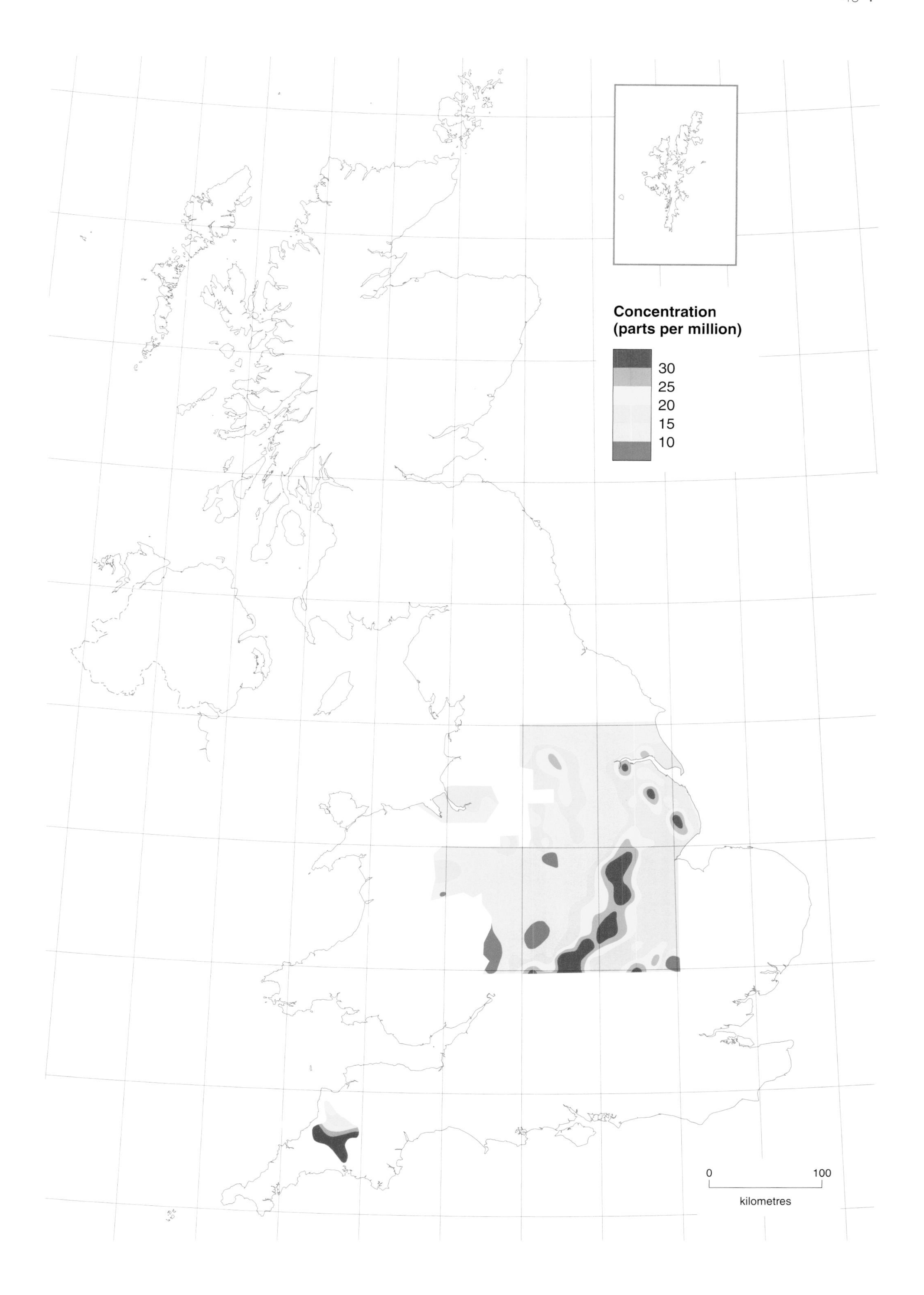
Concentration
(parts per million)
30
25
20
15
10
0
100
kilometres

Holbeck Hall Hotel, Scarborough, Yorkshire

Britain beneath our feet

Hazards

In comparison with many parts of the world, we live in a geologically stable region. Dramatic events such as volcanic eruptions or severe earthquakes no longer affect our country, although they are recorded in our geological history. Therefore, the cost to the UK of geologically related hazards, in the UK in terms of lives and assets, may come as surprise to many. The hazards we face may be more subtle, but their cost is significant. For example, between 2000 and 3000 deaths per year are attributed to cancers caused by radon gas, and the cost of damage to property resulting from heave and subsidence caused by the swelling and shrinking of clay, is estimated as being in excess of £3 billion for the last decade.

The following pages illustrate the variety of geological hazards that occur in Britain. They range from harmful gases, like radon and methane, to subsidence hazards such as landslides. Weak and soluble rocks can pose a threat to property and assets, and occasionally to life. Britain's mining heritage has left us with another legacy — the risk of collapse of old shafts and workings.

This section also describes geological information that can contribute to the assessment of flood risk in Britain — from both surface and groundwater — and two other themes provide an insight into the seismic hazards that have occurred in the past and may be expected in the future.

©Greenwich Council

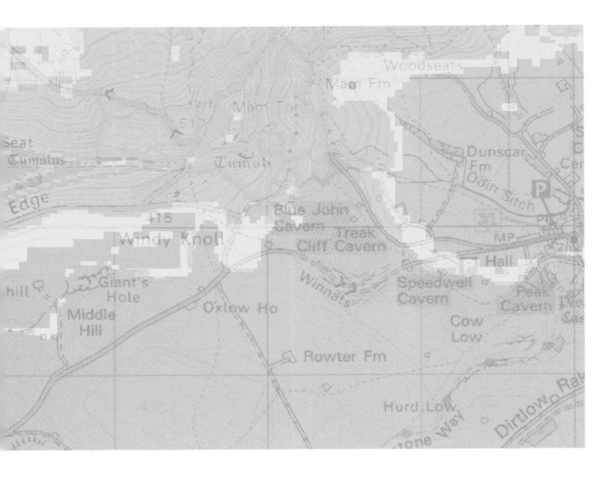

Hazards

Landslides

A landslide is the downward movement of ground under gravity. Movement may be relatively slow (slides) or fast (rockfalls) and may also affect flat ground above and below the moving slope. A slope remains stable while its strength is greater than the stress imposed by gravity. If the balance is disturbed, the ground moves until the stress is reduced or material strength is increased.

This map indicates the *potential* for landslides to be a hazard; not unexpectedly the potential hazard is greatest in areas with steep slopes. The detailed dataset that underlies this map is based on a combination of the most important factors that cause landslides. These factors include the type of geological material and its geotechnical properties, discontinuities (fractures, joints and bedding planes), slope angle and the position of the water table.

All the hazard themes are of relevance to planning, civil engineering and building design, insurance premium assessment and understanding, the threat to the stability of existing structures. In areas with significant landslide potential, material should not be removed from the bottom of slopes, nor should extra material be placed on such land. Slopes should be kept well drained by maintaining ditches. Tree planting on slopes enhances stability by encouraging root growth and removing moisture from the ground.

Landslide potential has been assessed using the 1:50 000 scale maps of bedrock geology and superficial deposits, together with information from several hundred thousand borehole records, scientific documents, engineering reports and photographs. The detailed digital data illustrated in the inset map are available as attributed vector polygons, raster grids, or in spread-sheet format, for example, by postcode district.

Landslide potential
Significant
Moderate
Low to nil
0
100
kilometres

Hazards

Swelling and shrinking clay

Some clays increase or decrease in volume as they absorb or lose water. These volume changes can cause, either swelling (heave) or shrinking (subsidence). In rocks that contain clay, the amount of volume change will depend on both the amount and the type of clay minerals present because some clays can absorb more water than others with a proportionally greater effect.

The map indicates the *potential* for shrinking or swelling of the ground to be a hazard. The problem is most widespread in southern and eastern England where young clay-rich rocks are at or near the surface.

Detailed information on the location and extent of swelling and shrinking clays is relevant to planners, landowners, engineers and householders and to those in the property transaction and insurance sectors. In areas where swelling and shrinking clays are a problem, foundations should be set sufficiently deeply to avoid the active shrink-swell zone and should be designed to resist lateral swelling pressures. Before planting or removing trees and shrubs near buildings sited in areas with significant shrink-swell potential it is advisable to seek professional advice.

Swelling and shrinking clay potential has been assessed using 1:50 000 scale maps of bedrock geology and superficial deposits, combined with information from several hundred thousand borehole records, scientific documents and engineering reports, photographs and geotechnical property values from the *National Geotechnical Properties Database*. The detailed digital data are available as attributed vector polygons, raster grids, and in spread-sheet format.

Photograph reproduced with permission of NHBC

Photograph reproduced with permission of NHBC

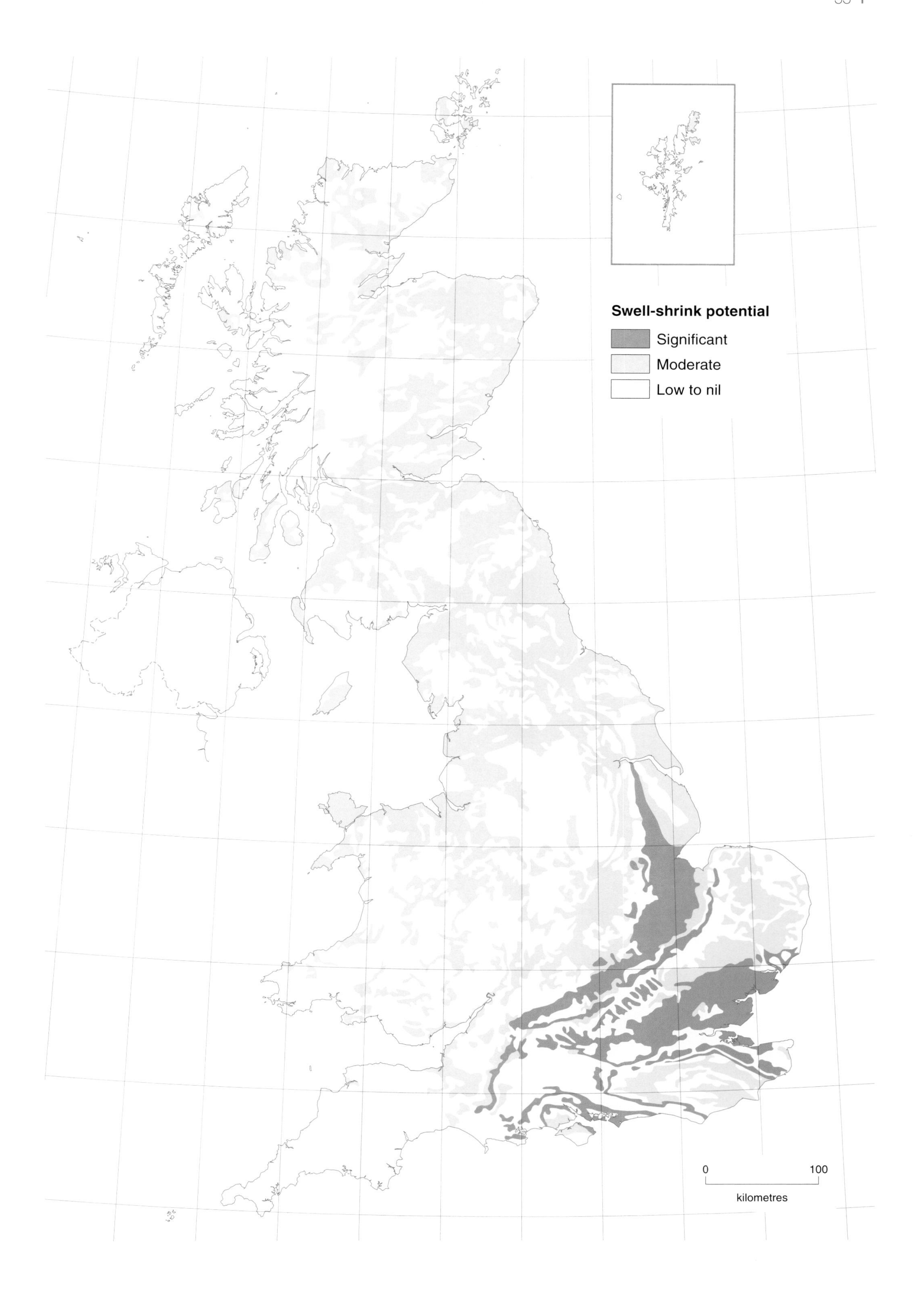
Swell-shrink potential
Significant
Moderate
Low to nil
0
100
kilometres

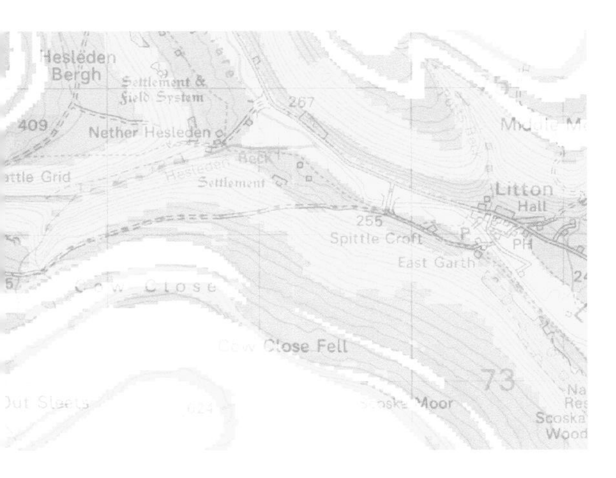

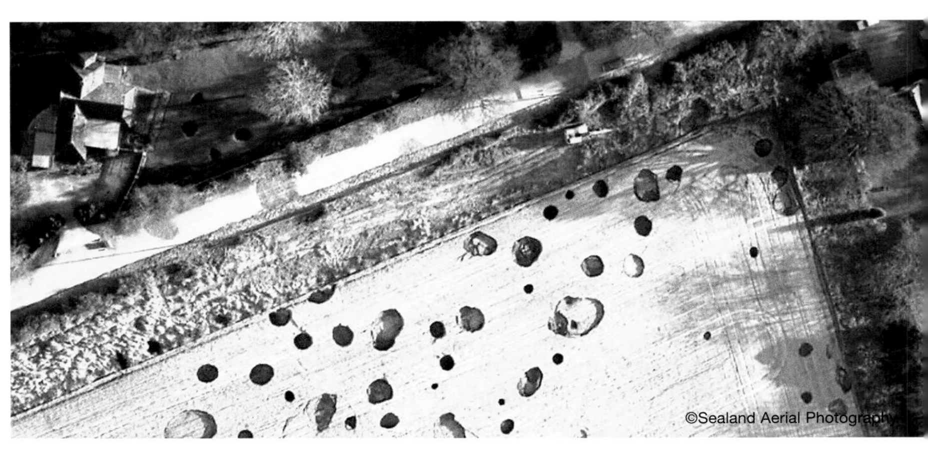
©Sealand Aerial Photography

Hazards

Soluble rocks

This map indicates the presence of soluble rocks that may cause a potential hazard. The factors that are included in the assessment of this hazard are the type of rock, the properties of the surrounding materials, the shape of the ground surface and the position of the water table.

Rocks that dissolve to cause hazardous ground conditions fall into three main types. These are:

- rock salt, or common salt, which dissolves quickly causing general subsidence except where being extracted
- gypsum (hydrated calcium sulphate), which dissolves less rapidly but can cause local subsidence and cavities
- limestone/chalk (calcium carbonate), which dissolves slowly to form underground cavities that rarely collapse but may cause local subsidence, significant pathways for pollution and an irregular rock surface below superficial materials.

The detailed data on which this map is based helps planners, landowners, engineers and householders to use land safely, maintain infrastructure efficiently and enables marginal land to be used beneficially by appropriate hazard management or avoidance. For example: in areas of soluble rocks, activities involving loading, infilling, excavation, surface drainage or changes to the water table may cause ground collapse, subsidence or groundwater pollution. Appropriate foundations such as raft or reinforced strip may be needed for safe construction. The data can be used to indicate whether there is a need for a site-specific assessment of the actual dissolution hazard when planning new buildings or change of land use.

Digital 1:50 000 scale geological maps of bedrock geology and superficial deposits provide the basis for this map. These data were combined with additional information on rock type, rock sequence, groundwater and ground surface contours. Also used were the records of known problems due to soluble rocks within the *Natural Cavities Database* and the *BGS Karst Geohazards Database*, BGS technical reports, borehole records and photographic collections.

Solution potential
Significant
Moderate
Low
0
100
kilometres

Hazards

Compressible and collapsible materials

This map indicates whether compressible or collapsible ground presents a *potential* hazard within an area. The method used assessed the presence of the most important factors that cause excessive or uneven settlement; these are combined, to give an overall assessment of the potential problem. The most important factors are the type of geological material, its geotechnical properties and microstructure.

Compressible and collapsible materials occur within young, near-surface geological deposits. As the map shows, compressible materials are associated with soft sediments in river valleys, coastal areas, fenland and peat moors.

In areas with significant potential for compression or collapse, uneven loading and changes to the water table (drainage or flooding) should be avoided. Appropriate foundations such as rafts or piles and flexible service connections may be needed. The detailed data, on which the map is based, provide invaluable context and help identify whether a site-specific assessment of the actual hazard and risk is needed.

The potential for compressible or collapsible material to be a hazard has been assessed using 1:50 000 scale digital maps of bedrock geology and superficial deposits. These have been combined with information from several hundred thousand borehole records, scientific documents, engineering reports and photographs. The detailed digital data illustrated in the inset map are available as attributed vector polygons, raster grids and in spread-sheet format.

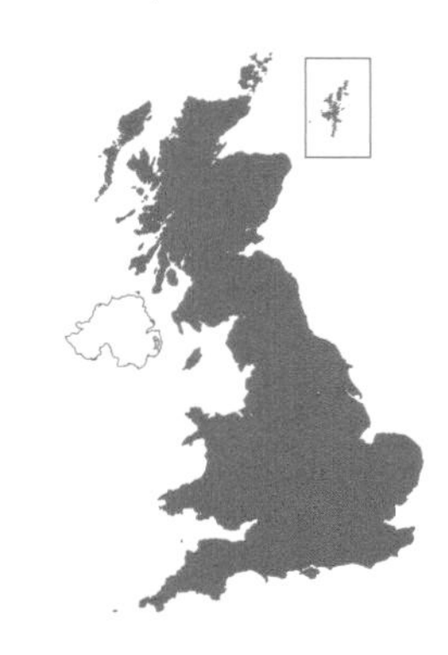

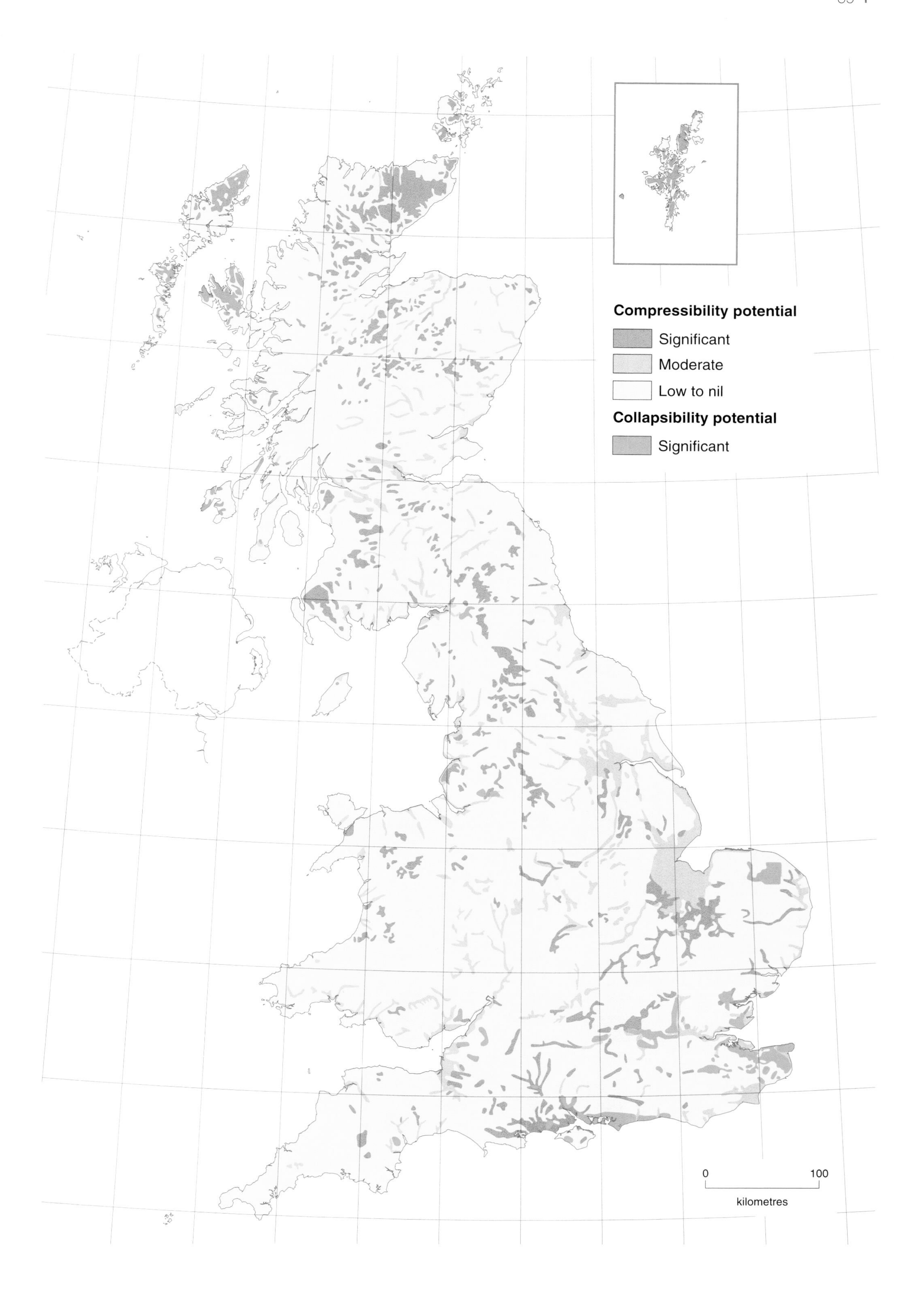
Compressibility potential
Significant
Moderate
Low to nil
Collapsibility potential
Significant
0
100
kilometres

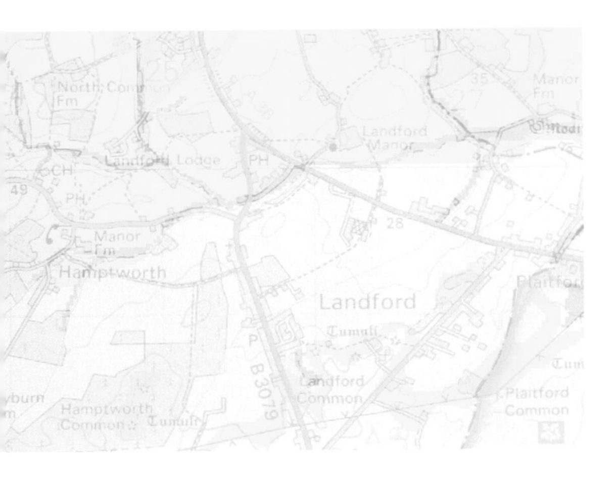

Hazards

Running sand

Running sand occurs when loosely packed sand becomes fluidised by water flowing through the spaces between the grains. The pressure of the flowing water reduces the contact between the grains and they are swept along in the flow. This may occur in a number of situations, for example where springs occur at the base of sand bodies, in excavations below the water table, and when saturated sand is vibrated during an earthquake.

The potential for sand to 'run' is assessed by combining information on the type of geological material, its geotechnical properties and the position of the water table. In Britain, running sand occurs widely in the alluvial deposits of the river valleys and, in the south-east, in uncemented bedrock deposits, such as the Thanet, Bagshot, Bracklesham and Barton sands. Problems are usually associated with construction activities such as excavation, tunnelling and dewatering or with leaking water supplies.

Information on where sand has the potential to run and to create a hazard is of interest to planners, landowners, engineers and householders. In areas with significant running sand potential, leaks in water services can pose a serious problem. There will be a need for groundwater control (dewatering or closed shuttering) during ground excavation. Irrigation or surface water disposal can have unforeseen consequences when running sand is present.

Running sand potential has been identified by using the 1:50 000 scale digital geological map data (both bedrock geology and superficial deposits) in combination with information from several hundred thousand borehole records, scientific documents, engineering reports and photographs. The detailed digital data can be made available if the form of attributed vector polygons, raster grids, or in spreadsheet format, for example, by postcode districts.

Running sand potential
Significant
Moderate
Low to nil
0
100
kilometres

Hazards

Radon

Radon is a naturally occurring radioactive gas produced by the radioactive decay of radium and uranium. Exposure to radon gas is considered to be the second largest cause of lung cancer, after smoking, in the UK. The map shows the likely potential for radon to be present in a given area. It is derived from a geological interpretation of indoor radon measurements in conjunction with permeability, uranium, soil gas radon, and ground and airborne gamma spectrometric data.

Geology is the most important factor controlling the source and distribution of radon. Relatively high levels of radon emissions are associated with particular types of bedrock and superficial deposits; for example some, but not all, granites, ironstones, shales rich in organic materials and rocks rich in phosphatic minerals. This generalised geological radon potential map shows those areas that are underlain, completely or in part, by geological units for which basic or full radon protective measures are indicated for new dwellings. The colour indicates the highest geological radon potential found within each grid square.

The geological radon potential data may be used to identify priority areas for monitoring radon in buildings in order to establish whether there is a problem and identify areas where radon protective measures may be required in new dwellings. The BGS digital geological radon potential data are used to provide a reporting service that indicates whether new homes and extensions may need to be protected from radon gas.

The reports are essential for builders and developers (and ensure compliance with Building Regulations). They are also invaluable for planners, architects and surveyors, who need to know what level of protection is required in new buildings. Access to the radon reporting service is available online at *www.bgs.ac.u/georeports/*.

The BGS geological radon potential data currently comprise 1:250 000 scale data with more detailed digital information for twenty 1:50 000 scale geological map sheets covering the most radon-prone parts of Derbyshire, Northamptonshire, Nottinghamshire, Leicestershire, Lincolnshire, Oxfordshire, Shropshire, Somerset and Yorkshire. BGS and the National Radiological Protection Board (NRPB) are collaborating on the production of more detailed radon potential information, based on a combination of 1:50 000 scale geological and 1 kilometre grid square mapping techniques. This will replace the current maps, published by NRPB, and will be used to provide advice to builders and developers as well as to householders and their legal advisers when a radon enquiry is made as part of property searches (CON29 [2002]: Standards Enquiries of Local Authority).

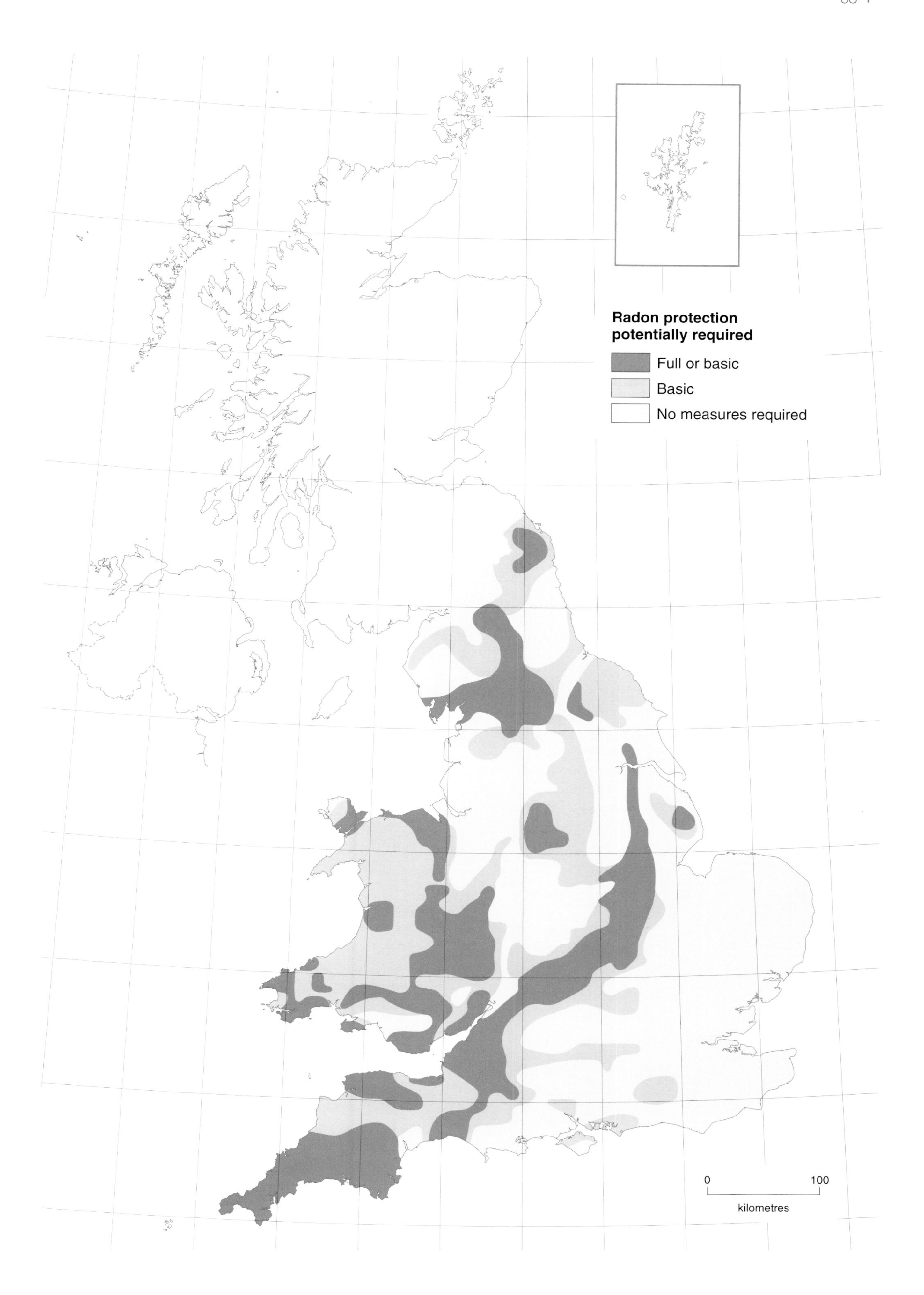
Radon protection potentially required
Full or basic
Basic
No measures required
0
100
kilometres

Hazards

Methane, carbon dioxide and oil seepage

Methane and carbon dioxide gases are asphyxiants and the former is explosive. Emissions of these gases from natural sources can be potentially hazardous to life. These gases may represent both short and long term hazards depending on factors such as the nature of the gas mixture, geological conditions, the proximity and extent of buildings, tunnels and mines and construction operations. Seepages of oil at the surface and underground appear to be a lesser hazard in the UK.

Explosion at Abbeystead pumping station

© Picture taken by Lancashire Evening Post

Methane and carbon dioxide emissions are associated with particular types of bedrock and superficial deposits, of which the most important are coal and peat. Other organic-rich rocks and unconsolidated deposits are also potential sources, for example carbonaceous shale, oil shale and bituminous shale, as well as organic-rich mud and silt in buried ponds, lakes or drainage channels. BGS susceptibility data classify different groups of rocks and superficial deposits according to the potential for encountering methane, carbon dioxide or oil accumulation in buildings or underground workings, including boreholes.

Where methane and carbon dioxide are likely to be present, caution must be exercised in planning. These hazards impose a constraint on development because of their implications for public health and safety. Developers should be aware of the potential problems that are associated with gas emissions and oil seeps. Employers at some places of work may have the responsibility of monitoring gas levels under the Health and Safety at Work Act, 1974.

The generalised susceptibility map opposite is based on 1:625 000 scale digital geological data, which have been combined with known locations of gas emission and oil seeps that have been recorded recently at the surface or in underground cavities. Production of the source map and dataset were commissioned by the Department of the Environment (now Office of the Deputy Prime Minister). A BGS report (WP/95/1) gives background information on the significance of gas emissions and oil seeps, provides details of the various sources of the data and evaluates their reliability.

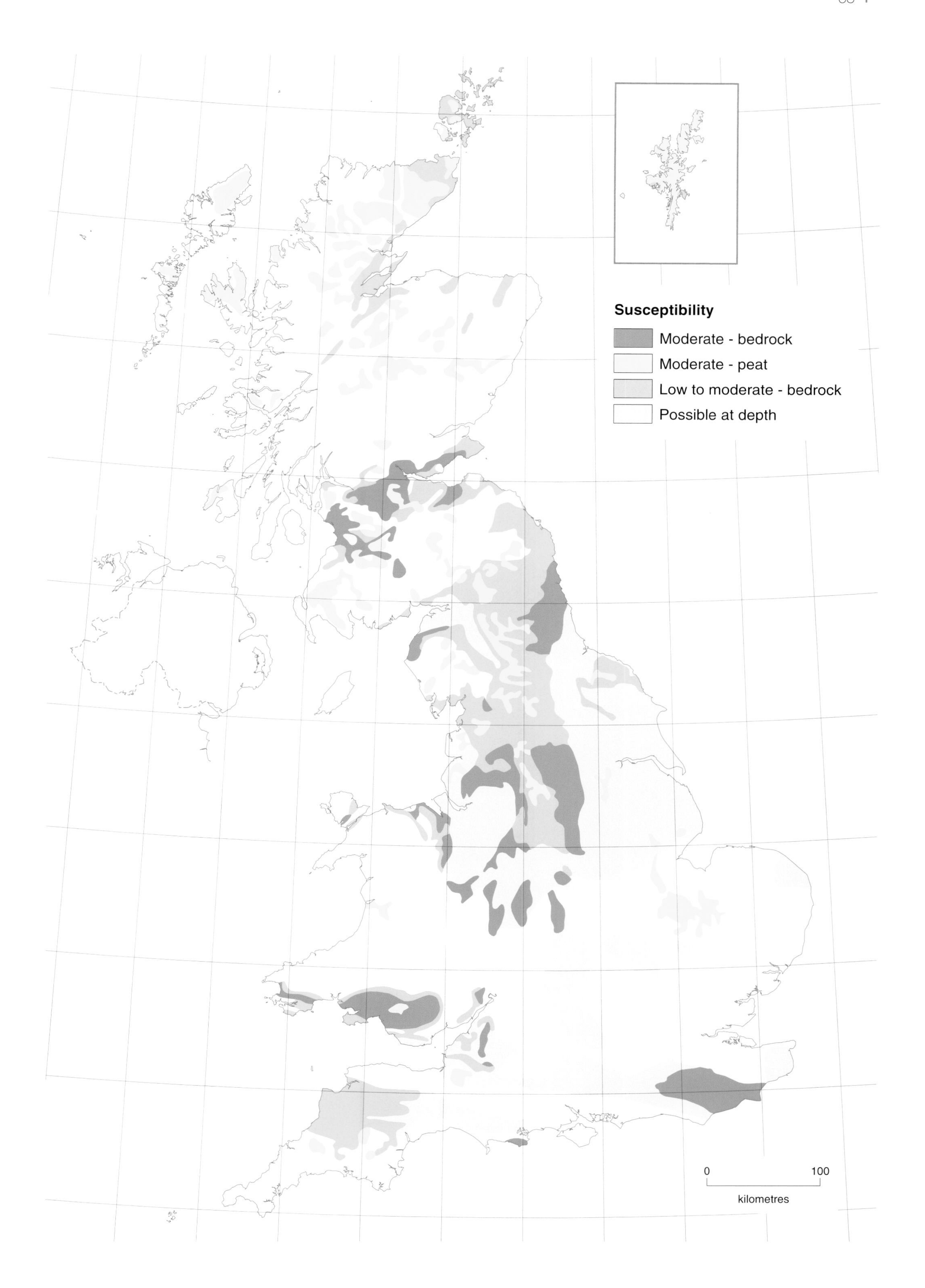
Susceptibility
Moderate - bedrock
Moderate - peat
Low to moderate - bedrock
Possible at depth
0
100
kilometres

Hazards

Earthquakes

BGS continually monitors seismic activity in the UK, and detects an average of 200 earthquakes each year. Modern instrumental data recorded at stations in the *UK Seismograph Network* complement historical information from the *National Seismological Archive*. Together, these data provide the UK with a comprehensive earthquake database.

BGS operates a network of seismograph stations throughout the UK to monitor both natural and man-made seismic disturbances on a long-term basis. Rapid access to the data enables BGS to give an immediate response to the occurrence, or reported occurrence, of significant seismic events. Each new earthquake adds to the database of seismic activity in the UK, which is used for seismic hazard assessment. The map shows those earthquakes in the database with a magnitude greater than 3.0 ML, which have occurred since 1382.

These data have a variety of applications. They illustrate the spatial distribution of earthquakes in the UK and are useful for preliminary site investigations, engineering projects and academic research. While large earthquakes do not occur frequently in the UK, a catalogue that covers a long period of time is essential in seismic hazard assessment.

Information held within the database includes the date, epicentre and magnitude for each earthquake and (where the information is available) origin time, depth and felt effects. The seismograph network has developed progressively over the years, and, as a result, the resolution of the data has improved so that earthquakes can be located with greater precision and accuracy than ever before. A basic version of the database, available for both onshore and offshore UK, can be viewed online at: *www.earthquakes.bgs.ac.uk* but more comprehensive information is also available.

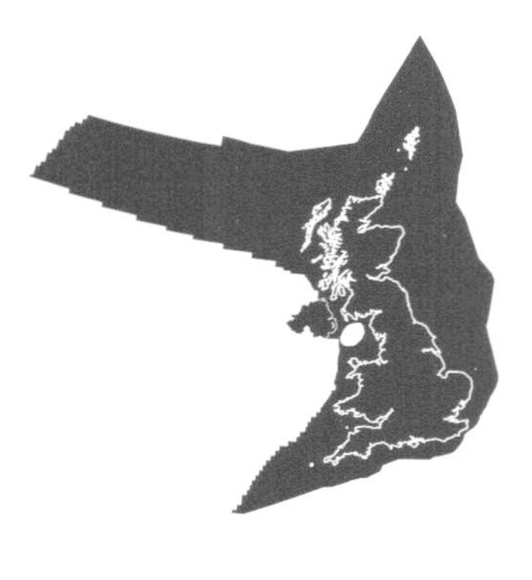

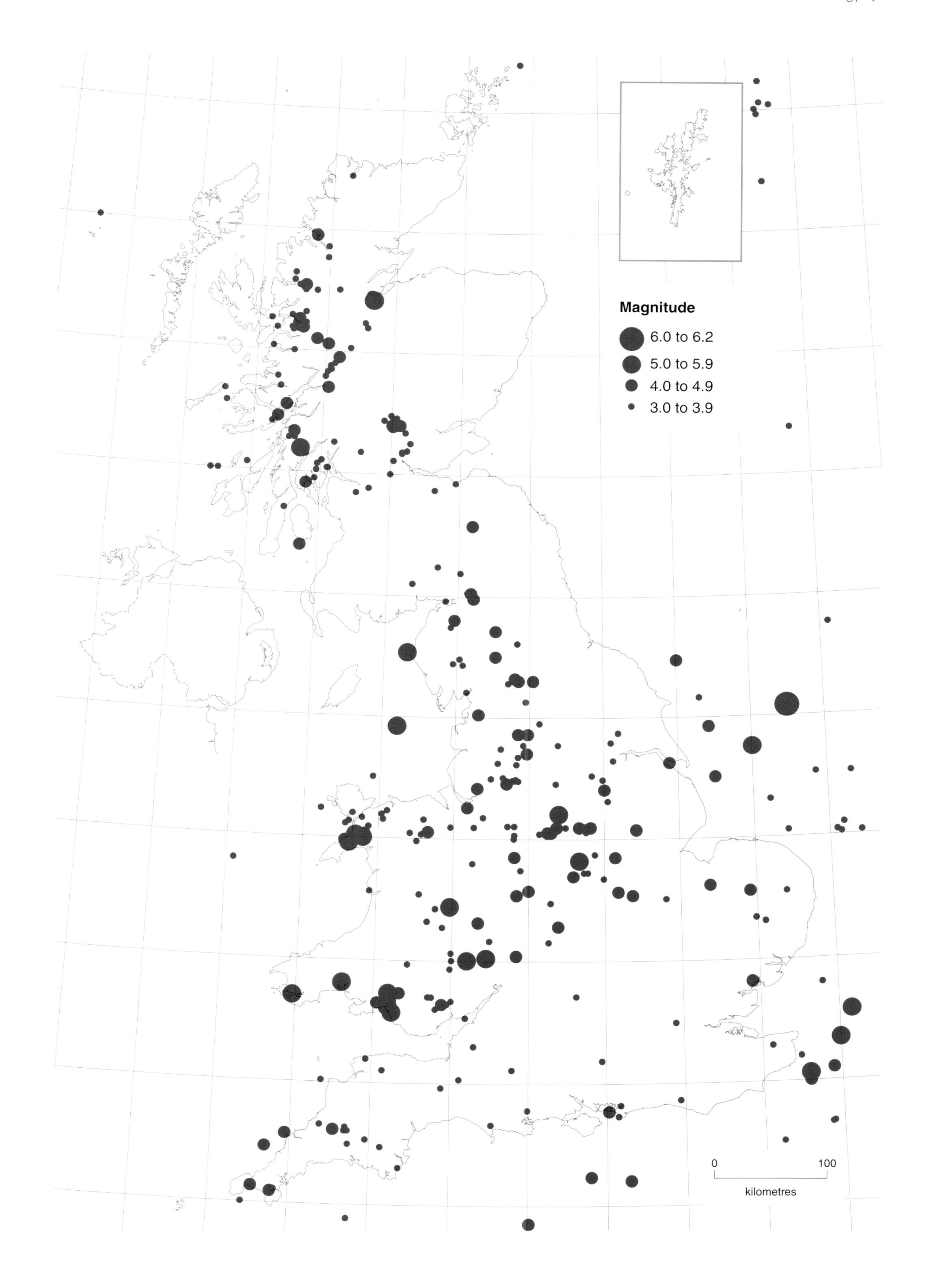
Magnitude
6.0 to 6.2
5.0 to 5.9
4.0 to 4.9
3.0 to 3.9
0
100
kilometres

Hazards

Earthquake intensity

The map indicates the expected strength of earthquake shaking likely to occur in Britain. This is shown as an intensity value that has a 10 per cent chance of being exceeded in the next 50 years. Intensity is a measure of the strength of shaking, and is classified according to the effects using a standard that is accepted internationally — the European Macroseismic Scale.

1=Not felt, 2=Scarcely felt, 3=Weak, 4=Largely observed, 5=Strong, 6=Slightly damaging, 7=Damaging, 8=Heavily damaging, 9=Destructive, 10=Very destructive

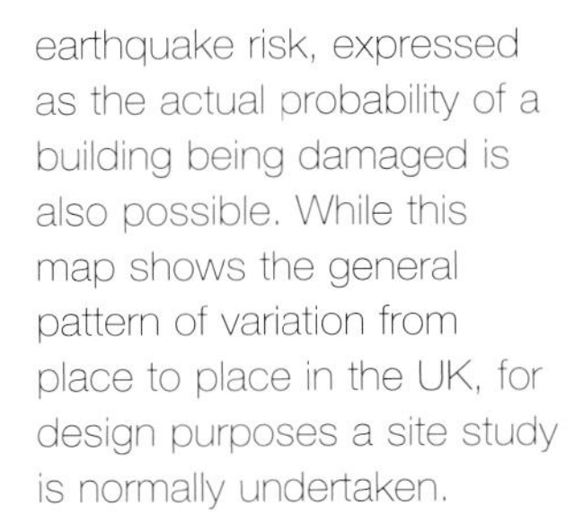

The map may be used to predict the expected strength of earthquakes that are likely to occur in Britain in the future. Since earthquakes cannot be forecast reliably, the best approach to modelling future events is to assume that the pattern of seismicity in the years to come will be broadly the same as in the past.

Earthquake hazard maps like this are more often expressed in terms of ground acceleration. Engineers regularly use such values in designing structures to be protected against earthquakes. However, intensity values as shown here are easier for people to relate to the actual experience of an earthquake. The model can also be used to calculate hazard in terms of acceleration or any other measure of earthquake shaking. The calculation of earthquake risk, expressed as the actual probability of a building being damaged is also possible. While this map shows the general pattern of variation from place to place in the UK, for design purposes a site study is normally undertaken.

The first seismic hazard maps for the UK were made by BGS about ten years ago. Since then, the maps have evolved to reflect improved knowledge about seismicity and subsurface geological structure and processes. The *UK Earthquake Catalogue* provides the fundamental data input to these hazard computations and is constantly updated. The relationship between strength of shaking, earthquake magnitude, and how intensity decreases with distance from an earthquake epicentre (attenuation) is known from detailed studies of hundreds of British earthquakes.

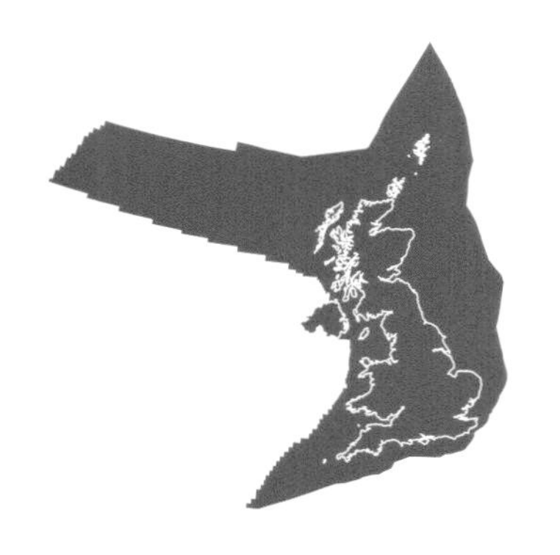

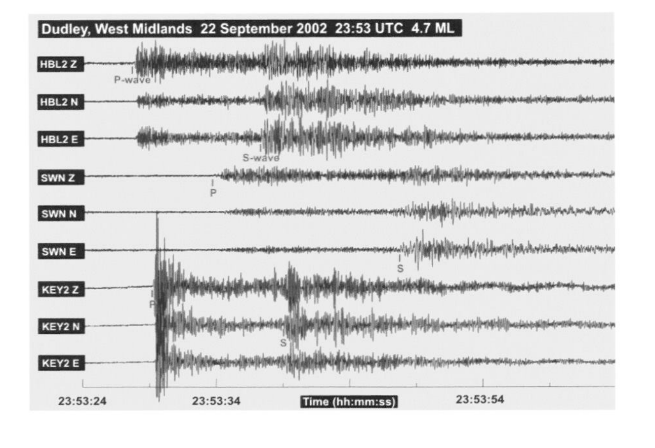

Intensity value
6
3
0
100
kilometres

Hazards

Groundwater flooding

Groundwater is usually considered an asset. It is the source of most of the water in streams and rivers, the origin of water for springs and the provider — through wells and boreholes — of clean water for farming, industry and public supply. However, it can create problems, especially when present in excessive amounts.

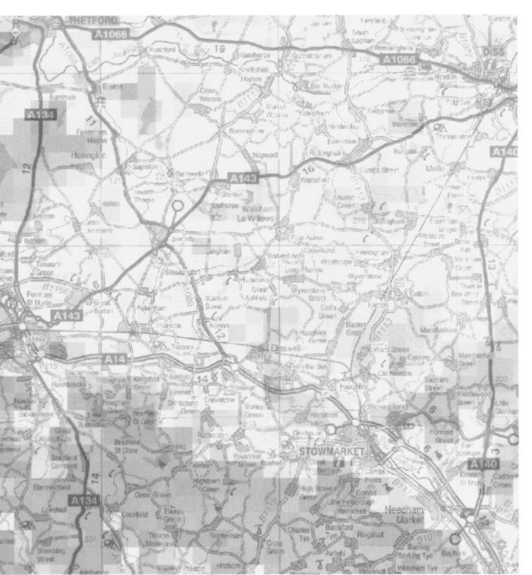

Water levels below the ground rise during wet winter months, and fall again in the summer as water flows out into rivers. In very wet winters, rising water levels may lead to the flooding of normally dry land, as well as reactivating flow in 'bournes' — streams that only flow for part of the year. The map opposite shows groundwater flooding potential over the Chalk of southern Britain. The Chalk shows some of the largest seasonal variations in groundwater level, and is thus particularly prone to groundwater flooding incidents.

Where land that is prone to groundwater flooding has been built on, the effect of a flood can be very costly. And because groundwater responds slowly compared with rivers, floods can last for weeks or months. Even before land is flooded, water may enter excavations and cellars. Locally, interaction between water in aquifers and in sediments in river valleys can affect the pattern and timing of flood events. As our understanding of the mechanisms of groundwater flooding increases, so does the prospect of flood forecasting, allowing property owners to take action to minimise damage and loss. The information that BGS holds on potential groundwater flooding can be used to guide land use planning and aid in the design of flood management schemes.

The data on groundwater flooding illustrated here are the product of integrating several datasets: a digital model of the land surface, digital geological map data and a water level surface based on measurements of groundwater level made during a particularly wet winter. This dataset provides an indication of areas where groundwater flooding may occur. More detailed assessments are possible for specific areas; these would use a combination of higher resolution digital mapping and individual records of groundwater level variation in wells and boreholes.

Flood potential
High
Moderate
Low
0
100
kilometres

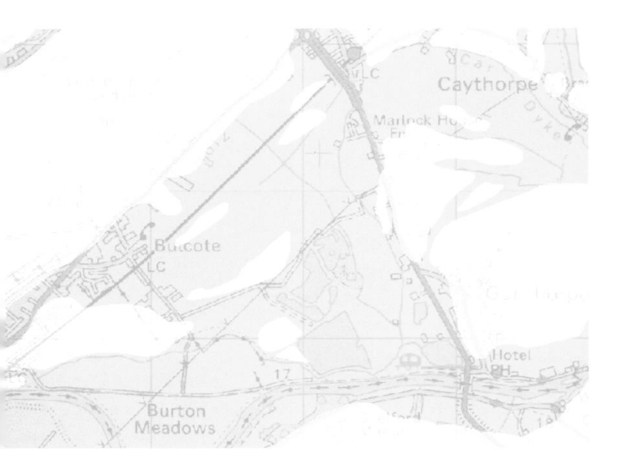

Hazards

Flooding in the recent geological past

Flooding is *the* major and most frequently recurring natural disaster in Britain. But it is not a new phenomenon and geological information shows where it has happened in the recent geological past — in the last 10 000 years. BGS holds data that show where the floodplains occur — the *alluvial deposits* that comprise clay, silt, sand and gravel left behind by previous inundations.

There is a very close relationship between mapped boundaries of alluvial deposits and areas that are prone to flood. Thus, geological information can be used to predict where flooding is most likely to occur. The geological map data can usefully complement, *but do not replace* other types of flood risk information that is available from sources such as high resolution topographic surveying, documented river levels and extent of floods.

The current cost of flooding disasters is high, but may increase as the more extreme effects of climate change unfold. The consequences of climate change for flooding are not easy to predict. The detailed analyses of the organisations involved in flood-risk modelling are normally restricted to events and parameters from the relatively recent past — the historical record. Thus, the long-term geological record may prove increasingly valuable.

Perversely, we are presently witnessing an increasing rate of building on flood plains and the Environment Agency has predicted that if this trend is not reversed, some 342 000 new homes could be built on floodplains in England and Wales in the next two decades.

Digital geological data which show the extent of alluvial deposits are available at 1:50 000 scale for virtually the whole of Britain; they delineate not only the wide floodplains of major rivers and streams, but also the flat ground that floors all of the smaller tributary valleys and gullies. This data should provide one component of a holistic approach to flood-risk modelling, and eventually deliver the type of detailed, high-quality information that will inform and provide solutions for planners, engineers, insurers and property owners.

Flooded in the recent geological past
0
100
kilometres

Hazards

Underground mining

Underground mining of minerals and rocks has taken place in Britain since 2700 BC. Over 36 different raw materials have been extracted, ranging from precious metals such as gold, to sandstone and gypsum. Voids caused by past mining activity pose a potential hazard, to both life and assets, and the risk of ground movement can affect property values. Further, underground workings and associated spoil can sometimes cause a pollution hazard.

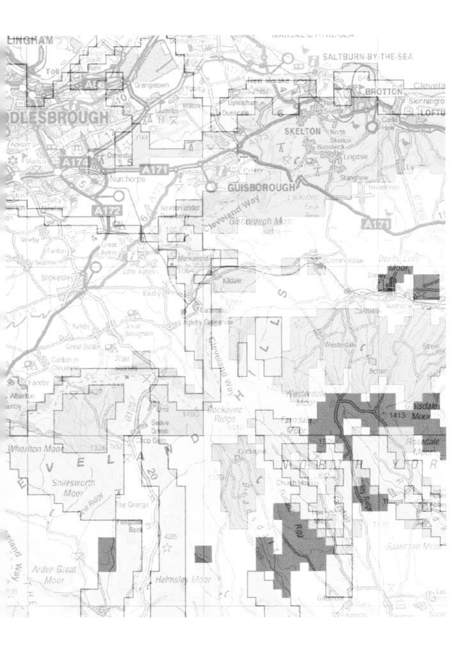

The coal mining areas of the UK are relatively well known, but fewer people are aware of other forms of mining, such as chalk mining in the south-east of England, or the underground mining of sandstone and limestone. At least ten minerals are still mined in the UK today. The map shows six categories of mining: metalliferous (nonferrous), rock, coal (and associated minerals), iron (mined outside the coalfields), chalk and evaporites.

Understanding the extent of past mining activity is extremely important in ensuring health and safety and the stability of property. But underground mining records also provide important historic and cultural information on the distribution and past extraction of mineral resources. They are a key source of information for geological surveying and scientific research.

The data that underpin the map opposite are derived from research undertaken by Ove Arup Ltd for the Department of the Environment and published in 1990. This source data show only the presence or absence of underground mining within the individual kilometre square. This information has been converted to *Geographical Information Systems* format by BGS. Definitive information on the actual extent of mining is available only by examining the original mine plans and sections. These plans are mostly in paper form, and exist at a variety of scales. Coal-mine plans are held by the Coal Authority and have been converted to digital form. The plans and sections for mines other than coal are held by many different organisations and individuals across the country, including BGS, but few are available in digital form.

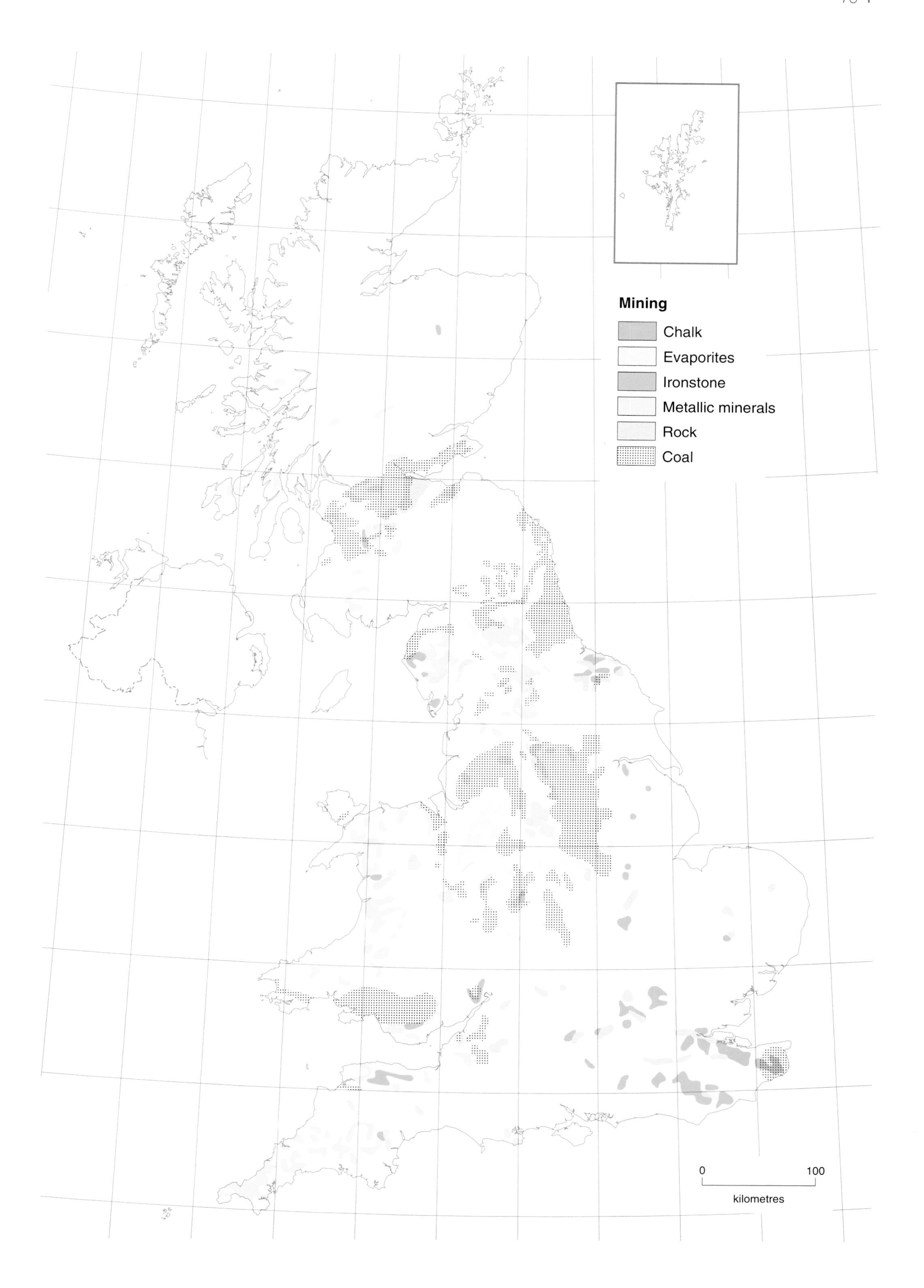
Mining
Chalk
Evaporites
Ironstone
Metallic minerals
Rock
Coal
0
100
kilometres

Cloud Quarry, Leicestershire

Britain beneath our feet

Resources

Britain's geological diversity has provided us with considerable mineral wealth and a range of energy resources such as coal, oil and gas. Industrial minerals include limestone, china clay and salt, and construction materials are widespread, for example sand and gravel and building stone. The Industrial Revolution in the 19th century was based on the exploitation of these resources and fuelled by cheap accessible coal. Although mineral extraction has declined or ceased, important production continues and provides essential raw materials for construction and manufacturing.

The themes in this section were chosen to illustrate the array of information that BGS holds on resources. The information describes the location and quality of the resources, and in many cases national, international production and commodity movement statistics are also recorded.

One theme in this section gives information on heat flow, a genuinely clean source of energy, and on the geothermal potential of the UK.

BGS is currently developing a high resolution *Mineral Information System* of all mineral resources on a regional basis. This *Geographical Information System* contains mineral resource and geological information as well as contextual planning and infrastructure information. The system is designed as a 'one-stop-shop' for planners, government, industry and other users. It is hoped that ultimately BGS will be able to offer this system for the whole of the UK.

Resources

Coal

Britain has a long history of coal mining. While the actual production of coal in the UK has declined significantly in the last few years, there are still major resources left in the ground. These have the potential to provide security of future energy supplies long after oil and natural gas are exhausted. The map opposite provides an overview of the coal resources of the country.

The map shows the areas where coal and lignite are present at the surface and also where coal is buried at depth beneath younger rocks. Conventional mining methods are not suited to working the deeply buried or offshore coal deposits. However, new technologies such as coalbed methane (CBM) and underground coal gasification (UCG) have the potential to provide a clean and convenient source of energy from coal seams where traditional mining methods are either impossible or uneconomical.

Coal resource maps for the whole of the UK have been produced by BGS as a result of joint work with the Department of Trade and Industry and the Coal Authority. The maps are intended to be used for resource development, especially coalbed methane, energy policy, strategic planning, land-use planning (including the encouragement of safe-guardianship of coal resources), the indication of hazards in mined areas, environmental assessment and as a teaching aid in historical and economic contexts.

BGS holds a variety of datasets relating to the UK coal resources, which are key to the possible future development of the resource. The datasets underpinning the map opposite were captured at a scale of 1:100 000. The data are available in *Geographical Information Systems* format.

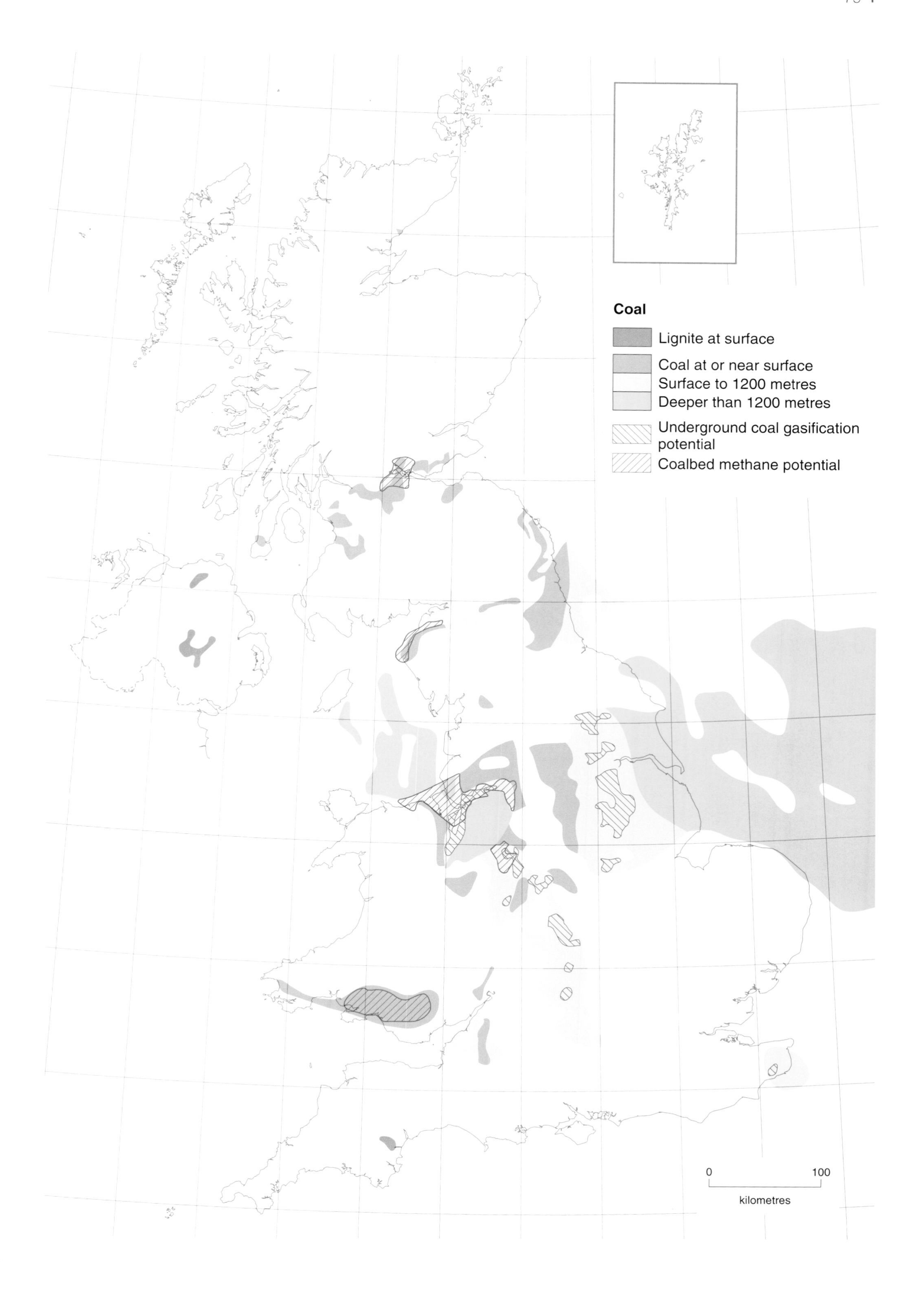
Coal
Lignite at surface
Coal at or near surface
Surface to 1200 metres
Deeper than 1200 metres
Underground coal gasification potential
Coalbed methane potential
0
100
kilometres

Resources

Industrial minerals

Industrial minerals include clay, salt and high purity limestone. They have many applications, for example clay is used in the manufacture of bricks and ceramics, salt in the chemical and food industries and high-purity limestone in cement manufacture. These minerals are essential for a wide range of economic activity within the UK and it is vital that they are developed on a planned, national strategic basis.

The map shows the distribution of a small selection of industrial minerals for which BGS holds detailed information. Salt is present in Cheshire and in the north-east and south-west of England. High quality limestone is located in northern, southern and eastern England, Wales and Northern Ireland. The map also illustrates the absence of these resources, for example over large parts of Scotland.

The extraction of minerals is becoming an increasingly contentious issue within Britain as large areas of the country are being placed under strict planning regulations that can make it difficult to develop a particular mineral resource. BGS is well placed to provide impartial advice to planning bodies at national, regional and local levels, on resource availability, quality and quantity, and the market for a wide range of industrial minerals essential to our quality of life. This advice allows decisions to be made in the context of national, regional and local need.

BGS holds an array of datasets (at a range of scales) on industrial minerals including ball clay, silica sand, china clay, brick clay, slate, potash, gypsum and barytes. Some regions of the UK are particularly well served (e.g. ball clay in Devon and Dorset) as a result of detailed investigations and surveys. Furthermore, BGS can offer information packages that place mineral information in context with other geological, planning and infrastructure information, which add significant value to the stand-alone industrial minerals database.

Mineral type
Limestone
Magnesian Limestone
Salt and potash
Ball Clay
Gypsum
0
100
kilometres

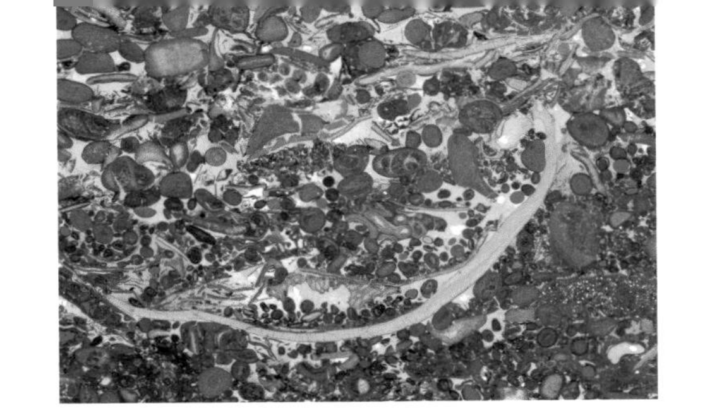

Resources

Building stones

Britain has been a major producer of building stone for hundreds of years. Because of our varied geology, a wide range of building stone types is available and this has influenced architectural style throughout the UK. This local distinctiveness is becoming increasingly valued and the maintenance of the built heritage is a growth area. Designers and architects are turning to natural materials for use in new constructions, including streetscape and paving schemes. This has lead to an increase in the demand for stone and a recognition of the value of our building stone resources.

The map shows just one component of the BGS building stone dataset: the location of significant building stone quarries throughout Britain. Large areas of Carboniferous rocks forming much of the north of England and the Midland Valley of Scotland are a major source of building stone. In contrast, the areas of older metamorphic rocks that form much of Wales and parts of the Lake District and the Highlands of Scotland are a major source of roofing slate.

Data on building stones is useful for strategic minerals planning and resource assessment, for example on a county or local authority basis. The information provides baseline data for reassessing the potential for future quarrying activity. Detailed information on both historic and active quarries is used for stone matching in order to select appropriate stone for repairs to historic buildings or for new construction in conservation areas and national parks. Attention to detail such as this is frequently required by planning regulations to be 'in keeping' with traditional architectural styles and materials.

BGS holds digital databases relating to building stone quarries, including both active and historic quarries, information on current operators, stone type, product and geological classification. BGS also has a materials collection that contains samples of quarried stone and thin sections for detailed microscopic analysis. The BGS *National Archive of Geological Photographs* contains a large number of images relating to building stones, including historic and recent images of quarries, stone samples and thin sections, many providing a unique record of a particular resource.

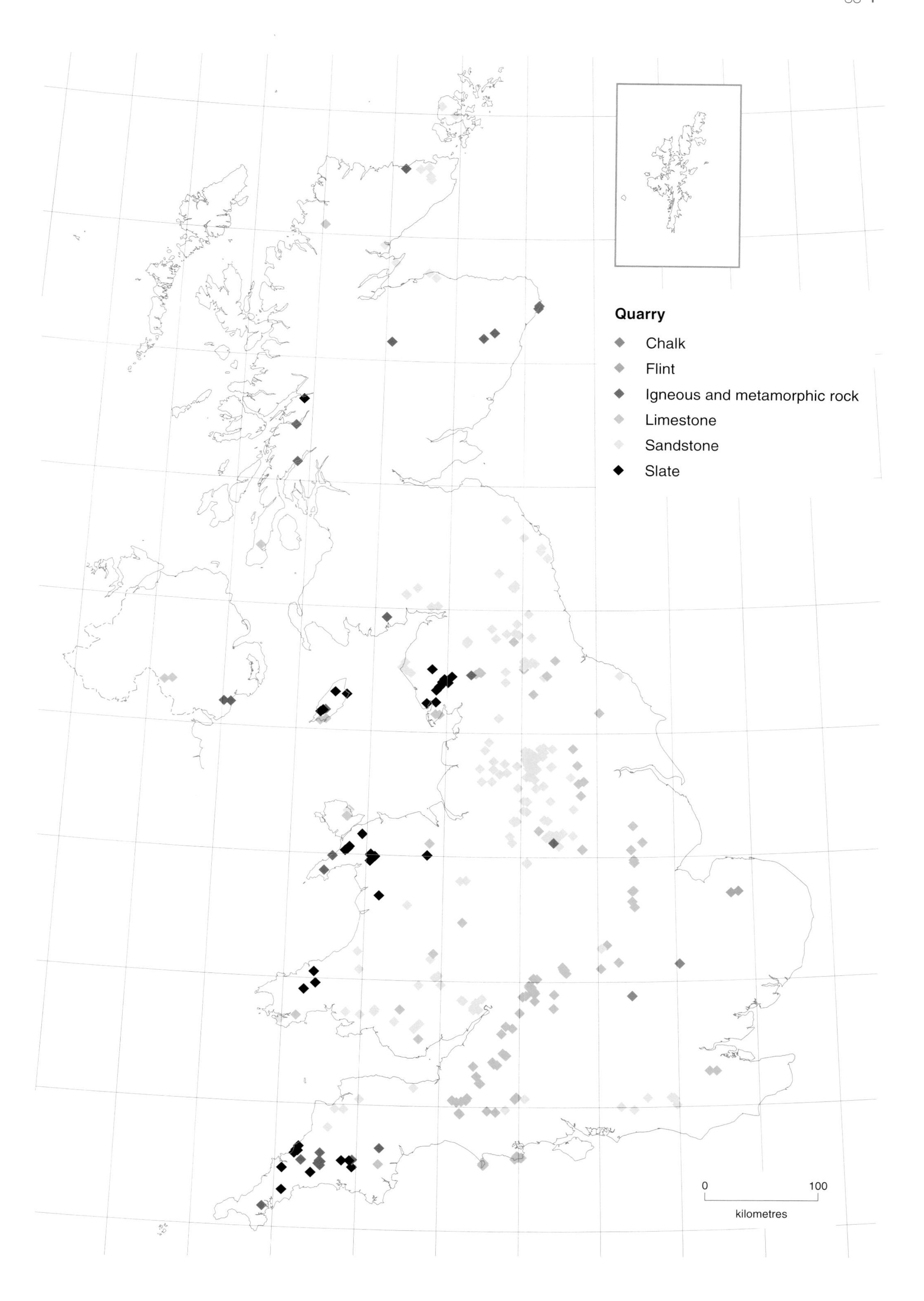
Quarry
Chalk
Flint
Igneous and metamorphic rock
Limestone
Sandstone
Slate
0
100
kilometres

Resources

Sand and gravel

Sand and gravel are essential commodities of the construction industry. Britain uses about 100 million tonnes per year in the construction of roads, houses, factories and shops. Sand and gravel is found within a range of geological settings both onshore and offshore. Knowledge of the distribution is crucial to national and local government, as well as the companies that deal with extraction and use.

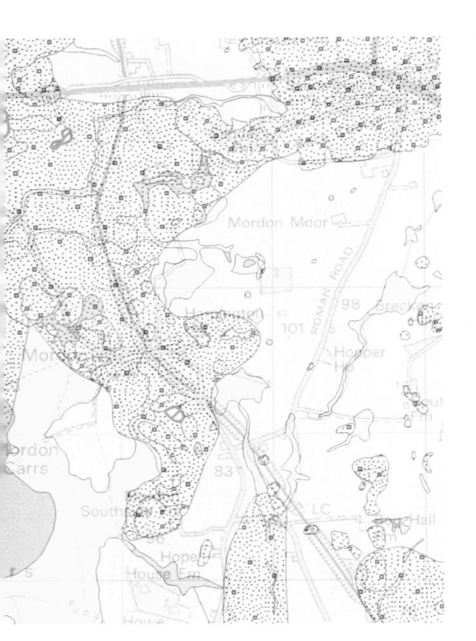

The map shows the distribution of sand and gravel, together with extraction sites in the UK. Sand and gravel resources are widespread across the UK, occurring within river systems, coastal dunes, glacigenic deposits (laid down by glaciers during the Ice Age) and may also be won from bedrock. It is not economic to transport sand and gravel over large distances — local markets require local sources — so the extraction sites are also widespread.

Information on sand and gravel is essential for the national and local minerals planning process. It can help to create informed opinion on the desirability of allowing deposits to be exploited and in avoiding the sterilisation of other deposits by development, such as housing. The BGS database can help quarry companies in the search for new deposits, allowing a rapid comparison of different areas. Sand and gravel deposits are variable and range considerably in particle size, shape and chemical composition. This variation is important, as it will determine what a specific deposit will be used for.

BGS holds a wide range of sand and gravel databases. Some of this information forms part of the generic *Superficial Deposit* and *Bedrock* mapping data. However, a prime dataset is a full digital spatial database of more than 12 500 purpose drilled boreholes, sample analyses and resource maps, which were produced, originally in paper form, by BGS for the Department of the Environment between 1967 and 1983. Additionally, the BGS *BritPits* database documents the nationwide distribution of active and disused mines and quarries.

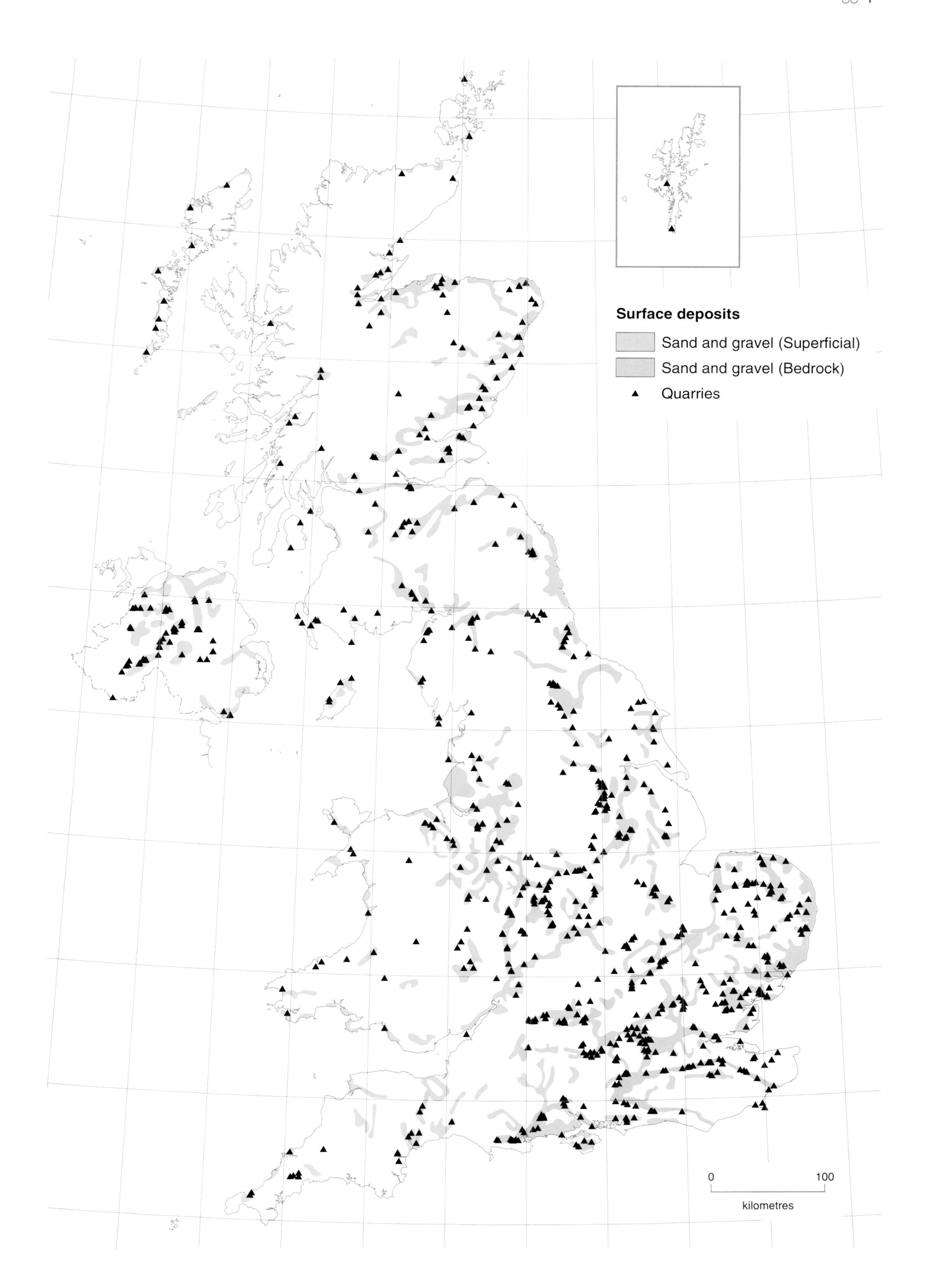
Surface deposits
Sand and gravel (Superficial)
Sand and gravel (Bedrock)
Quarries
0
100
kilometres

Resources

Metallic minerals

Metallic minerals have been important to human society since the end of the Stone Age. For example, copper is a metal that has been used for millennia and remains an essential component in modern high technology industrial applications. The UK has a long history in metal mining, and Cornwall was once a world-class mining field for tin. The UK still contains metal resources and the proving of viable deposits of both base metals and precious metals remains a possibility.

The distribution of gold, lead and tin in Britain is illustrated in this map. These three minerals are not present in the south-east of the country but are more abundant in areas where older rocks are exposed mainly in the north and west of Britain.

Metals are a fundamental resource for any modern society, and are traded internationally. Metallic minerals occur as large economically viable deposits only at relatively few locations across the world, and these are developed as mines that supply large areas of the globe. Metal prices rise and fall, and it is particularly during times of high gold and platinum prices that exploration companies become interested in the UK. A knowledge base of geological information for metallic minerals is essential for the assessment of the economic potential. Sensitive mining can give a major economic boost to an area and contribute to rural economic regeneration.

BGS has developed comprehensive databases for a number of metallic mineral occurrences in the UK. These databases can be used to assist exploration and mining companies. The *Mineral Occurrence Database* provides nationwide digital coverage of over 12 000 occurrences. These data complement other BGS products, such as geological, geochemical and geophysical data, which are all essential to mineral exploration. BGS also holds a *World Mineral Statistics database*.The UK is now wholly dependent on imports for primary metals supply and the database is a record of annual global production and trade in metallic and other mineral commodities essential to the UK's strategic planning in internationally traded mineral commodities.

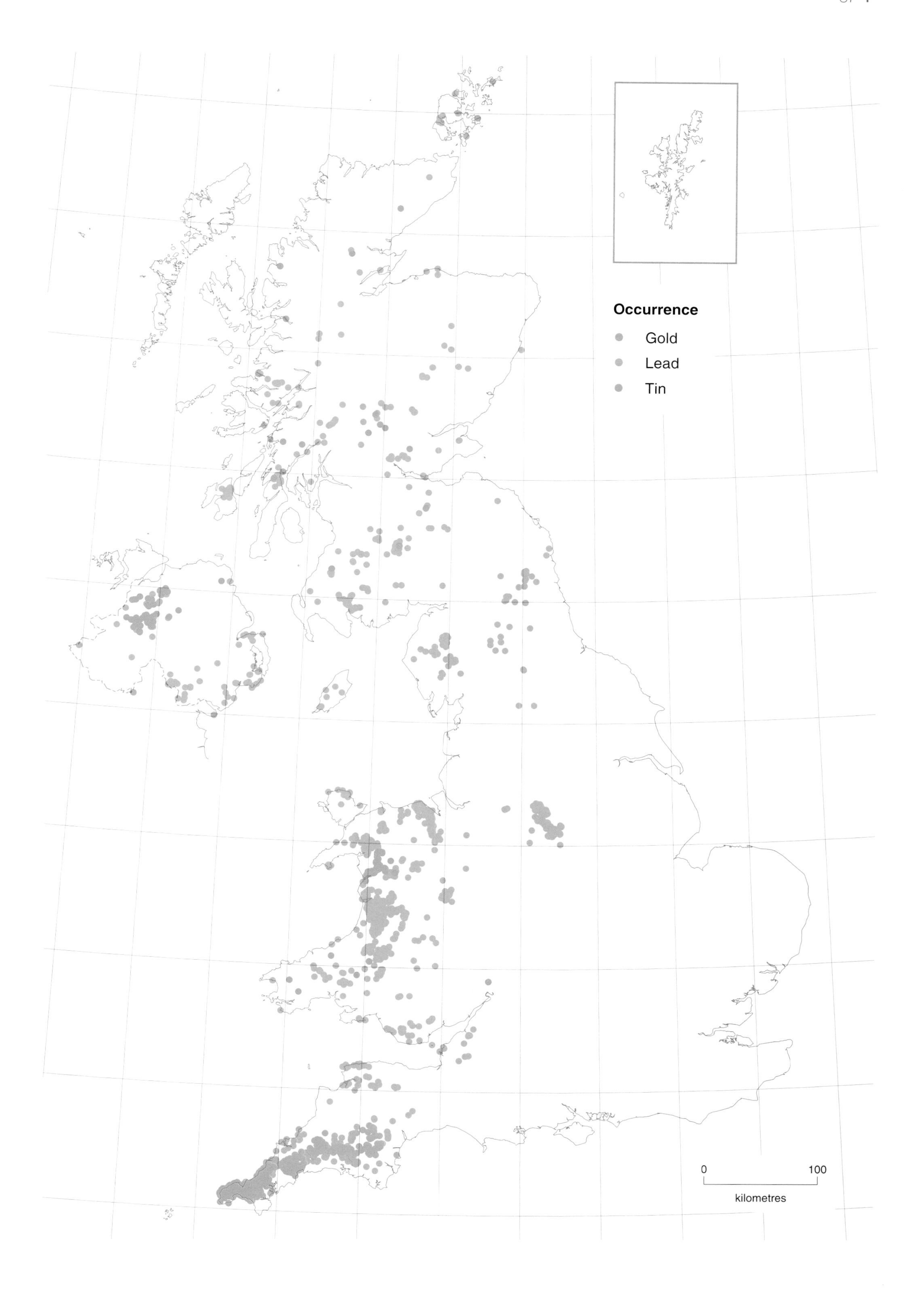
Occurrence
Gold
Lead
Tin
0
100
kilometres

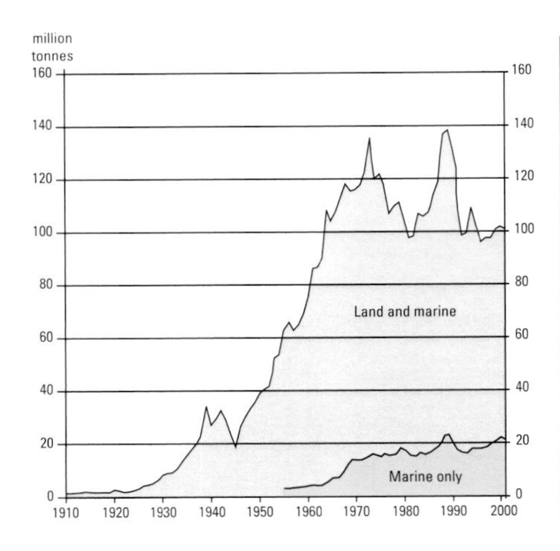

Resources

UK minerals production, supply and demand

The UK is an important producer and consumer of a range of mineral products that provide the raw materials for many sectors of the economy. The construction industry alone employs around five per cent of the UK workforce and underpins the national housing, road and rail infrastructure. BGS, in partnership with UK Government, generates and maintains comprehensive mineral databases that are essential for economic modelling and planning.

The map illustrates inter-regional flows within England and Wales for crushed rock. Rock such as limestone and granite is extracted and crushed at quarry sites throughout the UK. Most crushed rock is used for road construction and concrete manufacture. Supply and demand of crushed rock is uneven across the UK. High demand areas include densely populated regions such as the south-east of England. The high supply regions (e.g. south-west England) contain abundant rock resources.

Britain, as a highly developed economy, is reliant on mineral raw materials and processed mineral products to support the economy and quality of life of its citizens. BGS continually tracks the national production, consumption and trade across a wide range of mineral commodities and has developed a range of databases that form the primary national data source for mineral statistics. This information is regularly applied to economic and infrastructure planning. For example the materials required to build many thousands of new houses in the south-east of England must be sourced and transported in a planned and efficient manner.

Mineral commodity data include statistics for oil, gas, coal, metallic and non-metallic minerals (e.g. sand, gravel, ball clay, china clay, potash, fluorspar, barytes, silica sand and fuller's earth). The statistics, which are presented at national and regional level, are held digitally and can be supplied in spread-sheet format. A new interactive database is being designed to host this information for the longer term. Statistics, commentary and analyses are published annually by BGS as a book and *pdf* document (*UK Minerals Yearbook*).

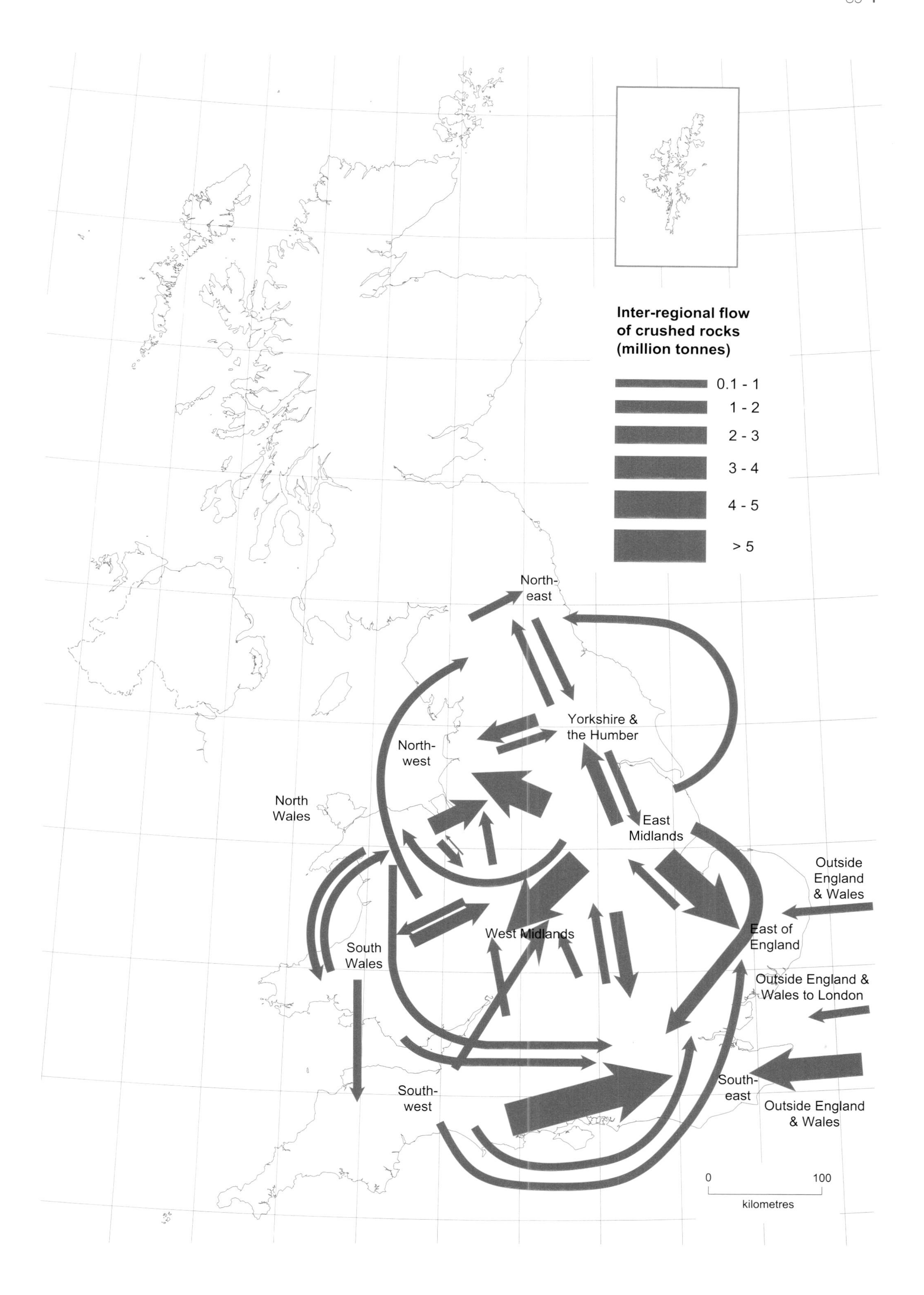
Inter-regional flow of crushed rocks (million tonnes)
0.1 - 1
1 - 2
2 - 3
3 - 4
4 - 5
> 5
North-east
Yorkshire & the Humber
North-west
North Wales
East Midlands
Outside England & Wales
West Midlands
East of England
South Wales
Outside England & Wales to London
South-west
South-east
Outside England & Wales
0
100
kilometres

Resources

Heat flow

The surface temperature of the earth is determined predominantly by the radiant energy from the sun. However, a small amount of heat is conducted upwards from the subsurface, and this map illustrates the variations in this component. When combined with information about the thermal conductivities of different rock types, heat flow data can be used to predict deep subsurface temperatures, which helps in assessing the potential geothermal energy resources.

Terrestrial heat flow has a value across much of the UK of 40 to 70 milliwatts per square metre (mWm^{-2}). Values are locally above 130 mWm^{-2} in parts of Devon and Cornwall where the crust contains radiogenic granite with a high heat production. About 25 per cent of the measured data are from sites above granites, although these rocks outcrop over less than 10 per cent of the area. About 20 per cent of the data are in south-west England. If these data are excluded, the distribution becomes normal with a mean value close to 58 ± 16 mWm^{-2}.

It should be emphasised that individual observations of heat flow in the sedimentary crust can be considered as providing only the apparent conductive heat flow, modified to some unknown extent by convective flow. Local anomalies in the heat flow field can be useful indicators of hydrodynamics, but are generally identified only where data are especially concentrated.

Understanding the heat flow field is important for deep subsurface temperature modelling, geothermal resource estimates and deep repository models. Subsurface temperature tends to increase with depth, on average at about 26°C per kilometre, but locally at a very different rate depending on heat flow and thermal conductivity. In some parts of the UK geothermal gradients are in excess of 35°C per kilometre.

This map is based on about 200 measurements from heat flow boreholes and over 500 estimates of heat flow from deep boreholes. Measured heat flows are based on equilibrium temperatures and measured thermal conductivities for that borehole. Estimates of heat flow are computed from measured 'bottom hole temperatures', and the mean thermal resistance of the rocks penetrated by the borehole. There are little data available for Wales and Scotland.

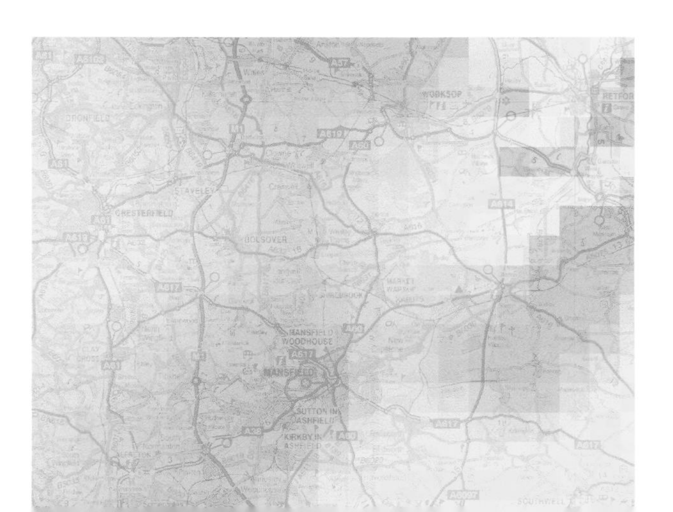

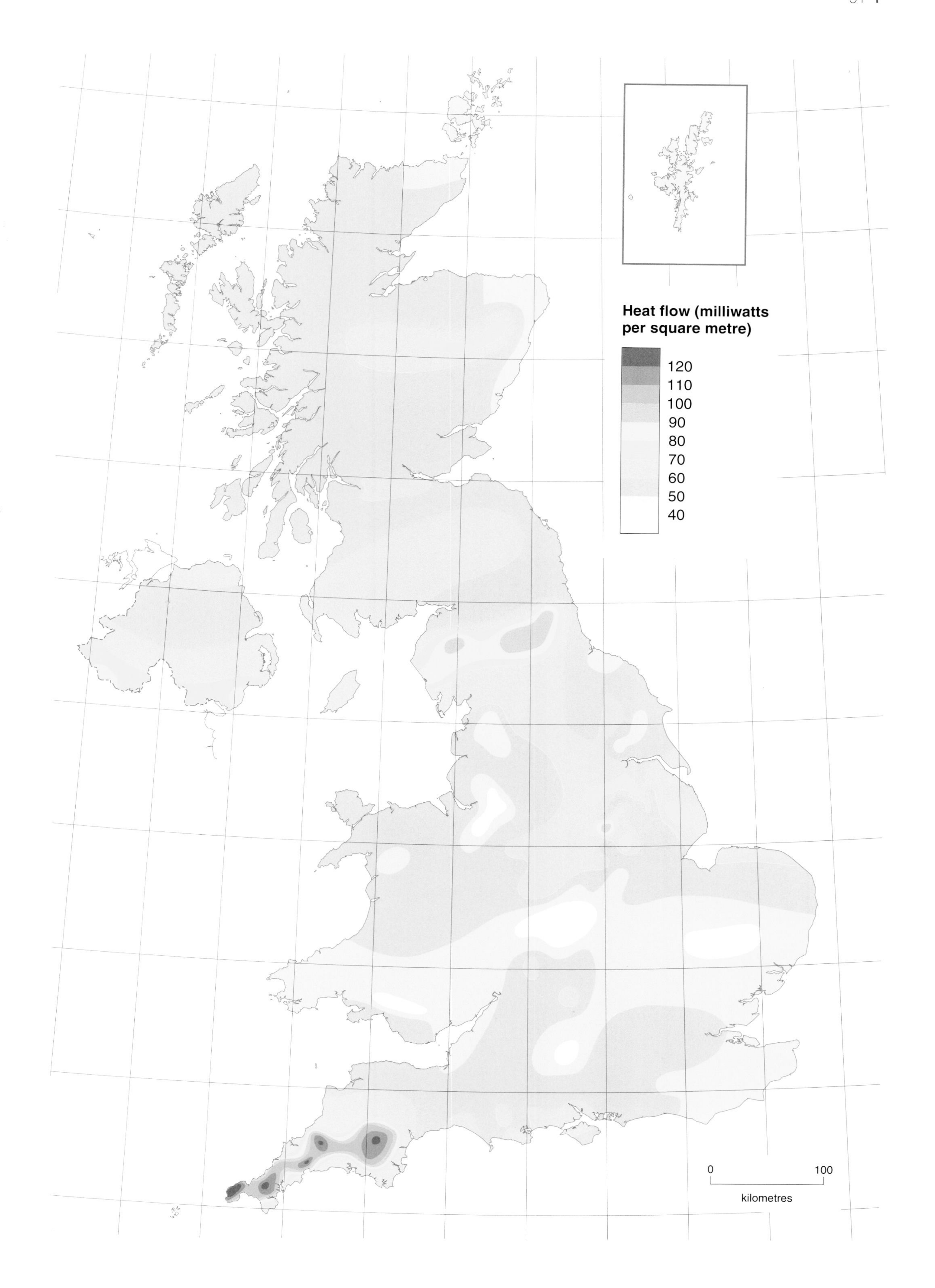
Heat flow (milliwatts per square metre)
120
110
100
90
80
70
60
50
40
0
100
kilometres

Britain beneath our feet

Offshore and coastal

The UK Continental Shelf Designated Area extends to up to 600 miles offshore and covers an area of more than 850 000 square kilometres, about 3.5 times larger than the UK land area. However compared with the land surface, our understanding of the nature and form of this submarine domain is limited. It is an area that contains our greatest relief with high sea-mounts and areas of very deep water. It is the source of our largest energy resource and it is dramatically dynamic, nowhere more so than in the coastal zone.

The development potential of the offshore and coastal area is considerable (as are the hazards it presents and our ability to pollute it). The rocks beneath the sea are well known as a source of oil and gas, but less so as the possible location of carbon dioxide sequestration to address global warming. Fishing is a major offshore industry and we exploit the sea bed for sand and gravel, excavate it for pipelines and cables, and are now developing offshore wind, wave and tidal power. But how much do we understand about the long-term effects of these activities on sediment transport and marine habitats?

New techniques for surveying the sea bed using swath mapping will revolutionise the understanding of the marine landscape and result in more detailed maps and a better understanding of the processes active in the marine environment. Detailed studies of changes in the sediment patterns will give us new evidence on how the marine environment reacts to climate change.

We already know a great deal about our marine landscape, but many questions remain. For over 30 years BGS has been surveying the sea bed around Britain and the rocks beneath. The themes in this section are intended to provide an introduction to the type of data, information and knowledge that BGS can provide. This includes sea bed sediment data, assessments of coastal erosion and submarine geological hazards, models of the deep structure of the rocks and their resources.

Offshore and coastal

Bathymetry

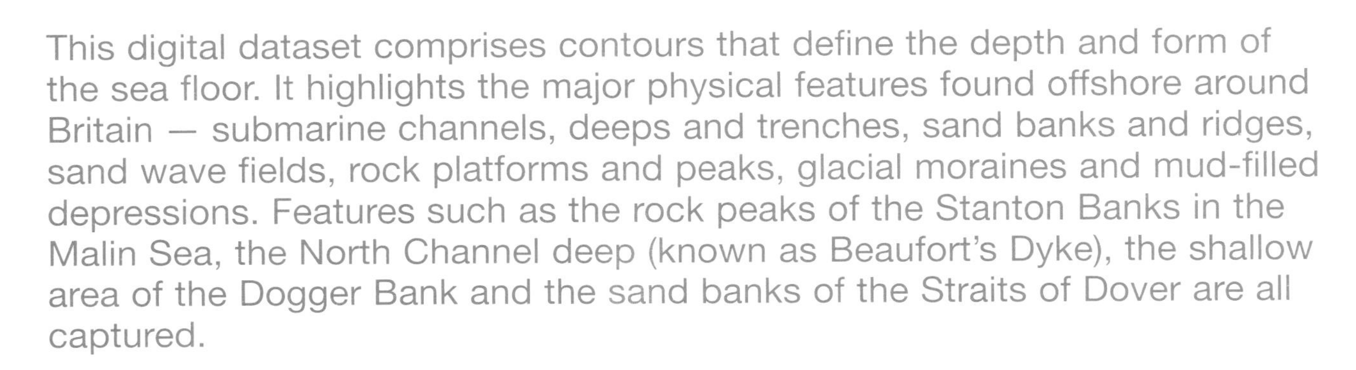

This digital dataset comprises contours that define the depth and form of the sea floor. It highlights the major physical features found offshore around Britain — submarine channels, deeps and trenches, sand banks and ridges, sand wave fields, rock platforms and peaks, glacial moraines and mud-filled depressions. Features such as the rock peaks of the Stanton Banks in the Malin Sea, the North Channel deep (known as Beaufort's Dyke), the shallow area of the Dogger Bank and the sand banks of the Straits of Dover are all captured.

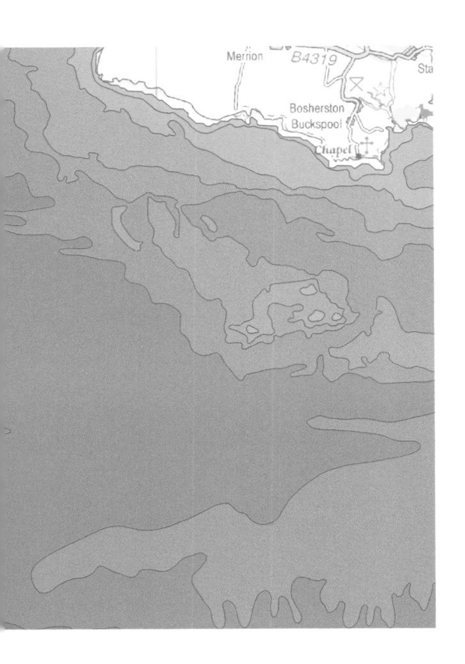

The dataset (known as *DigBath250*) is proving of value to a variety of users with interests in research, planning, developing and exploiting the sea and sea bed. It has been produced to provide a regional-scale digital bathymetry as a primary dataset for mapping and modelling of the sea bed. It may also prove useful for modelling tidal, current and water-column data. Applications include oil and gas development, renewable energy from wind, wave and tides, fisheries, aggregate extraction, environmental monitoring, marine and coastal planning and legislation. It is not, however, a navigation chart and has been produced for non-navigation use only.

DigBath250 (*www.bgs.ac.uk/products/digbath250*) is a vector-attributed digital bathymetry of UK and adjacent European waters in *Geographical Information Systems* format. It is being developed in partnership with the UK Hydrographic Office. Version 1 covers all UK and adjacent Irish waters. It is currently being extended to include all of the North Sea, English Channel and South-west Approaches. The attributed contours are at intervals of 10 metres between 0 and 200 metres depth, 20 metres between 200 and 400 metres, and 100 metres at depths below 400 metres. Two primary sources of data were used to compile the contours. First, over 200 000 kilometres of survey data were collected by BGS during regional surveys. Second, UK Hydrographic Office charts and survey data have been used to compile or improve the bathymetry where BGS data were not available or were inadequate.

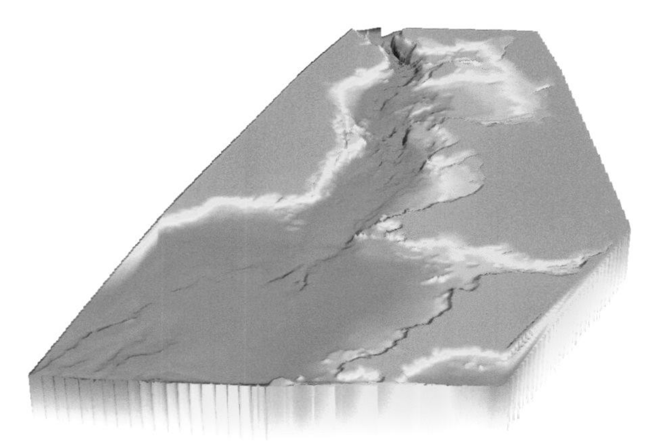

Depth (metres)
0
50
100
200
500
1000
1500
2000
2500
0
200
kilometres

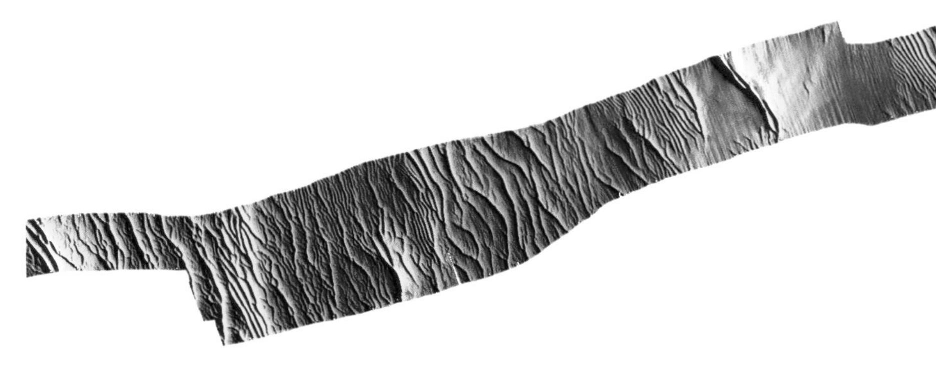

Offshore and coastal

Sea bed sediments

The character and distribution of sediment on the sea floor are important in understanding the nature of the marine environment. The sediments provide evidence of present and former depositional environments, and reflect the influence of the topography of the sea bed and the effects of tides and currents.

The sediments originate from numerous sources including ancient rivers and glaciers, which crossed the sea bed during ice ages when sea level was low. They have then been moved and re-worked by waves and tides as sea level rose to give us the pattern of sediment distribution that we have on the sea floor today.

Any development or activity on the sea bed requires knowledge of the nature of the sea bed sediments. The information is valuable for tidal and current modelling and sediment transport studies. It has numerous applications including habitat mapping, offshore renewable energy, oil and gas development, aggregate extraction, fisheries, environmental monitoring, marine and coastal planning and legislation

The BGS sea bed sediment classification scheme that has been used is based on the proportion of mud, sand and gravel analysed from grab and core samples.

Over 28 000 samples were collected by BGS during the offshore survey programme around the UK. Sidescan sonar records, which can map the distribution of sand waves and rock outcrops on the sea bed, have also been used to delineate some of the boundaries on the map. The detailed dataset (see inset) is known as *DigSBS250* and it was produced by digital capture of data from a series of 1:250 000 scale sea bed sediment maps published by BGS.

Ivor Rees, BGS © NERC

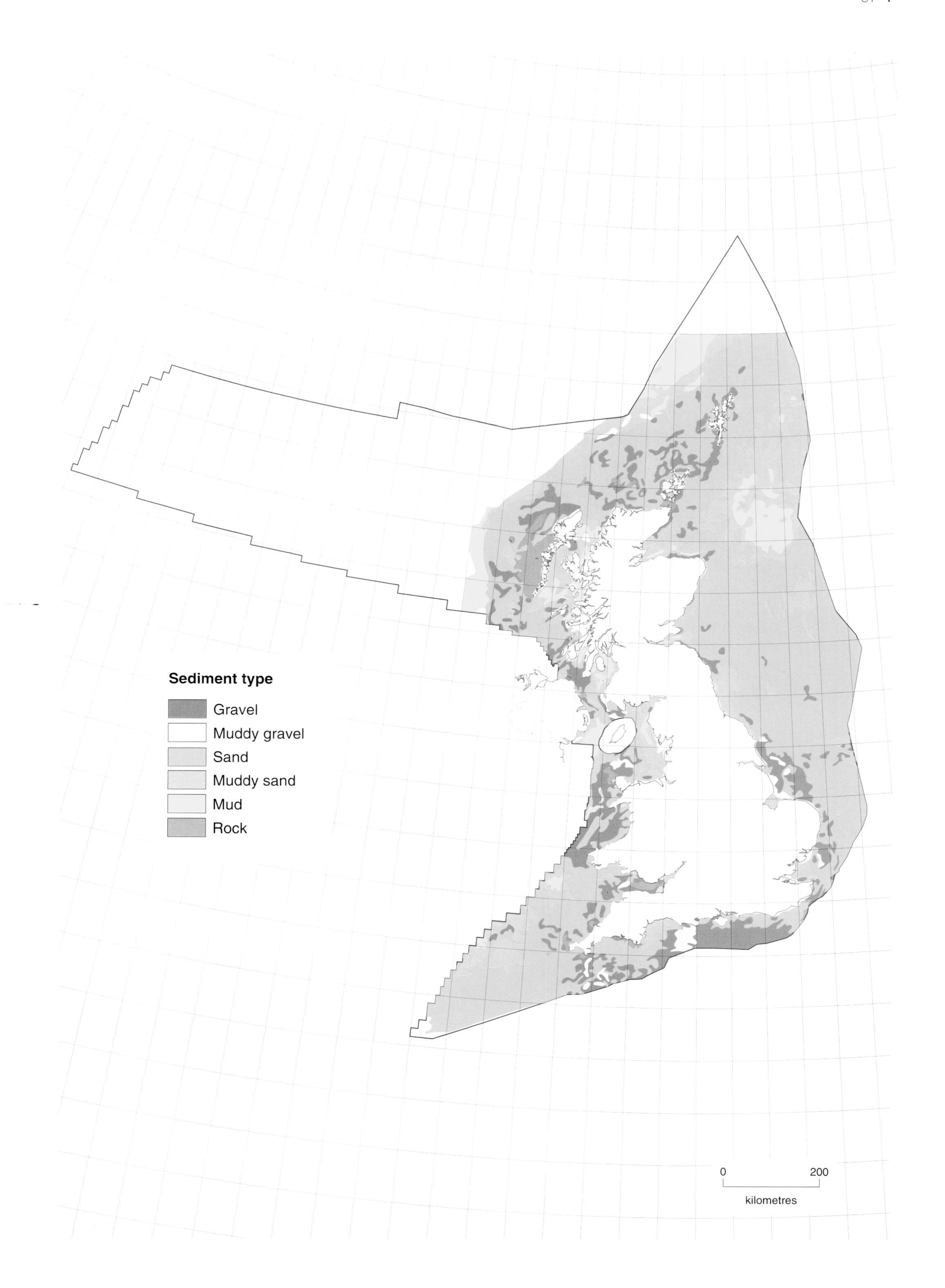
Sediment type
Gravel
Muddy gravel
Sand
Muddy sand
Mud
Rock
0
200
kilometres

Offshore and coastal

Quaternary deposits

The Quaternary period commenced about 2.6 million years ago. During that time a number of glacial and interglacial cycles have occurred and are associated with changes in sea level of the order of 100 metres or more. Sediments that were deposited during this period, and now underlie the sea bed, vary greatly in thickness, composition and age. These variations have contributed to the rich and diverse modern sea bed habitat, but they may present difficulties to those involved in offshore development.

Knowledge of the Quaternary and sea bed sediments provides key information linking coastal and submarine evolution, and gives us an insight into climate change during that period. Maps of these deposits help us to understand and to evaluate how offshore resources can be developed in a safe and sustainable manner. They are useful consultation documents in the granting of exploration licences and other consents, and in identifying the range of possible hazards that developers are likely to encounter, prior to detailed site investigations.

Geophysical data (both profile and swath) and sample data have been collected during ship-borne operations since 1969. Profiles are spaced at 8 to 15 kilometres apart on the continental shelf and approximately 20 kilometres apart on the continental slopes. Deeper basins have profiles averaging some 40 kilometres apart. On average, samples have been collected at one sample per 43 square kilometres on the continental shelf, and about one sample per 200 square kilometres or more on the continental slope and rise. Sediment sample cores have been taken from depths ranging from 30 to 100 metres or more below the sea bed.

Deposit type
Gravelly mud and sand
Mud
Mud and sand
Sand
Gravel
Mud, sand and gravel undifferentiated
<5 m thick
0
200
kilometres

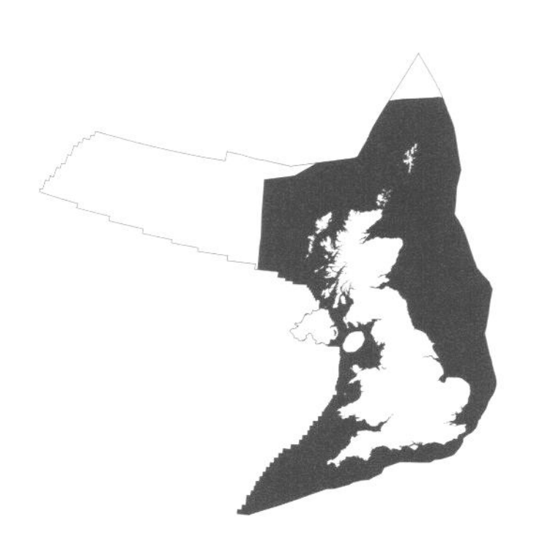

Offshore and coastal

Thickness of Quaternary deposits

Unconsolidated Quaternary deposits cover more than 95 per cent of the UK offshore territory. Thickness of these sedimentary deposits varies from a few centimetres to more than 800 metres. This variation can be attributed to erosion and deposition associated with former glaciations, changes in sea level and the structure of the submarine basins. Information on the thickness of the Quaternary deposits is essential in planning offshore developments.

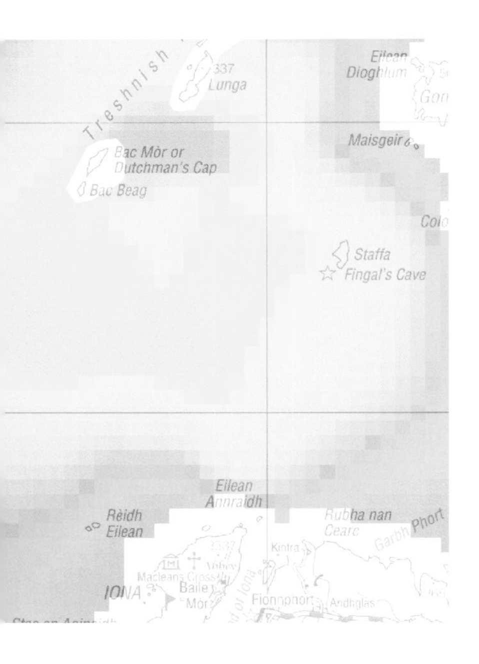

Data on the thickness of the mobile sea bed sediments and underlying Quaternary deposits combined with information on composition (see page 98) allow us to understand the link between sediment sources and sediment sinks. These are significant factors in understanding both coastal and near-shore evolution and offshore habitats.

Thickness data also allow us to estimate the likely extent and depth of resources, for example aggregates, and to understand marine geological hazards, which are particularly important in planning engineering projects offshore.

Profile and swath geophysical data and sample data, collected between 1969 and 2003, provide the detailed digital information on which this generalised map is based. Information on the *white zone* — the near-shore zone between Low Water Mark and about 15 metres depth — has not been presented because of the general lack of data in this zone.

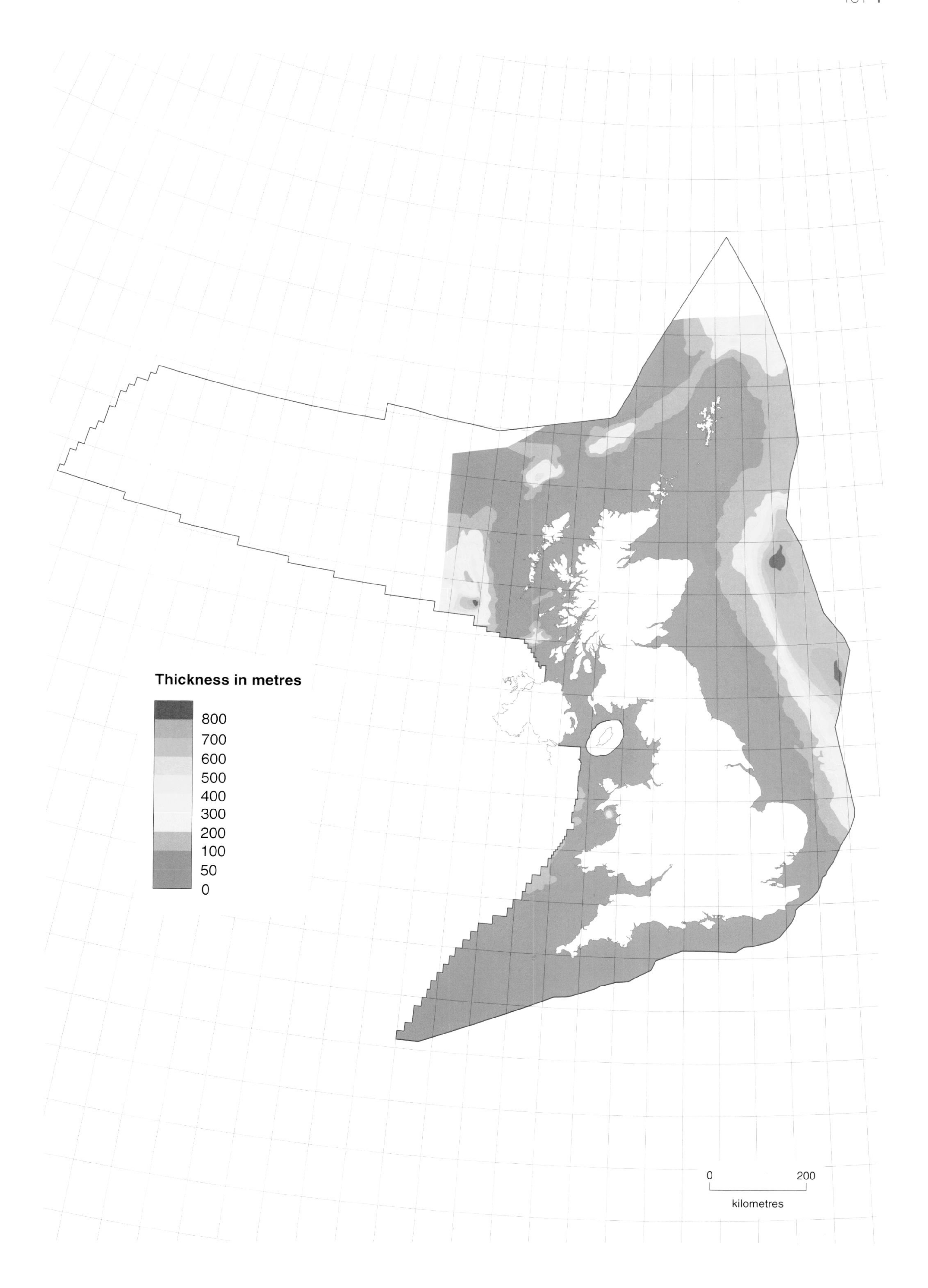
Thickness in metres
800
700
600
500
400
300
200
100
50
0
0
200
kilometres

Offshore and coastal

Bedrock geology

The rocks that occur beneath the sea bed sediments and Quaternary deposits range from approximately 2.6 million to more than 590 million years old. They extend from the coast to water depths of 2000 metres or more. The composition of these rocks, depositional history and subsequent deformation have contributed to the rich variety of UK offshore oil and gas prospects and resources. The structure of rocks beneath the sea bed has given the UK some wonderfully diverse submarine landscapes.

Bedrock geology maps are important in allowing us to identify and assess oil and gas resources, and help in the development of these resources in a safe and sustainable manner. Now, they also play a key role in evaluating the potential for storing carbon dioxide at depth offshore. Civil engineering installations, for example wind farms, telecommunication and pipeline routes, also depend on an understanding of the geological context, which these maps provide.

Since1969, BGS has collected geophysical traverse data and grab, shallow core and borehole sample data for the purpose of offshore regional mapping. More than 400 shallow boreholes drilled by BGS have been used to confirm and calibrate variations in bedrock geology. Subsequently, data from these have been combined with interpretations of released commercial seismic surveys and oil and gas well data to compile databases, maps and reports.

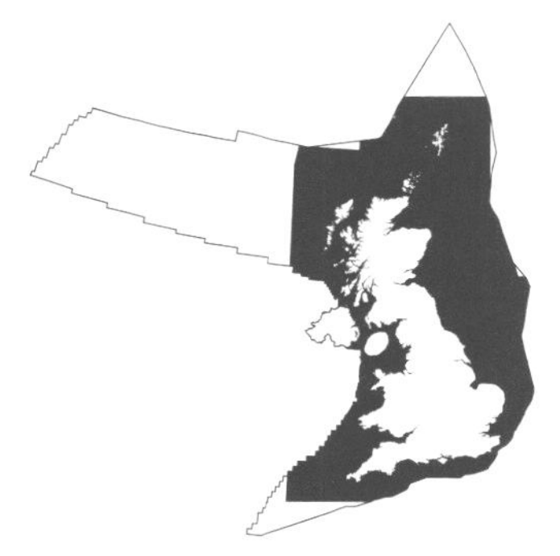

Age - millions of years
65
142
206
248
290
354
417
443
495
545
Neogene - Palaeogene
Cretaceous
Jurassic
Triassic
Permian
Carboniferous
Devonian
Silurian
Ordovician
Cambrian
Archaean - Proterozoic
0
200
kilometres

Offshore and coastal

Geological hazards

Geological hazards exist on the coast and offshore. More than 40 different types of hazard have been identified, resulting from either individual conditions or a combination of conditions. Regional and site-specific assessments of geological hazards have become pivotal in planning the exploration and development of offshore and coastal sites.

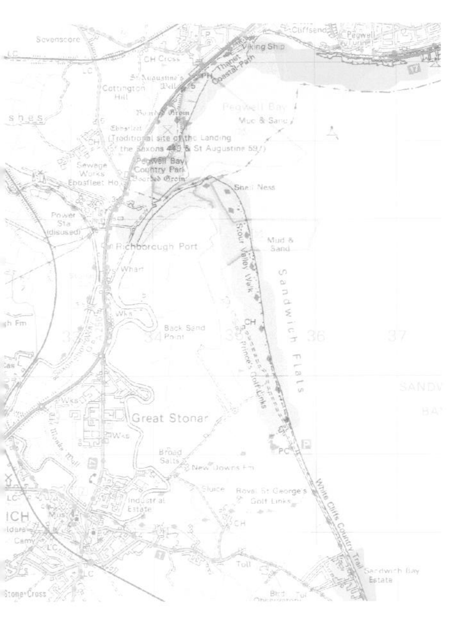

Two hazard types are illustrated here: susceptibility to coastal erosion based on rates of cliff recession and offshore gas hazards.

Locally, the rates of coastal erosion vary greatly. In parts of southern and eastern Britain, the rate may exceed 15 metres per year in places. But generally in northern and western Britain the rate is extremely slow. The overall susceptibility is governed largely by geological properties. In some areas, the accumulation of sediment results in the formation of new land.

Where gas occurs close to the sea bed, sediment strength is commonly altered, either by gas pressure or associated cementation of the sediment. In deep water, methane may occur in an ice-like form known as hydrate (a potential resource). When disturbed this can release large quantities of methane and destabilise sediments, perhaps causing landslides. The released methane would also constitute a hazard if it were to reach the surface as it is a potent greenhouse gas in the atmosphere.

Other hazards, such as ground instability and mass movement, have onshore equivalents, but some, for example mobile sea bed features such as sandbanks, are unique to coastal and marine systems.

Analysis of geological hazards is part of assessing and classifying the natural risks that submarine or coastal operations may encounter. Developments requiring assessment of geological hazards include:

- drilling
- trenching and foundation engineering
- piling and foundation engineering design for the exploitation of both non-renewable and renewable energy resources
- planning for cable routes
- determining the effects of overburden stripping and waste disposal as a result of site preparation or industrial aggregate and mineral extraction.

The data sources used in assessing offshore and coastal geological hazards typically include site-specific survey reports, digital maps and records of sea bed sediments, superficial deposit and bedrock geology, geophysical survey results, scientific papers and technical literature.

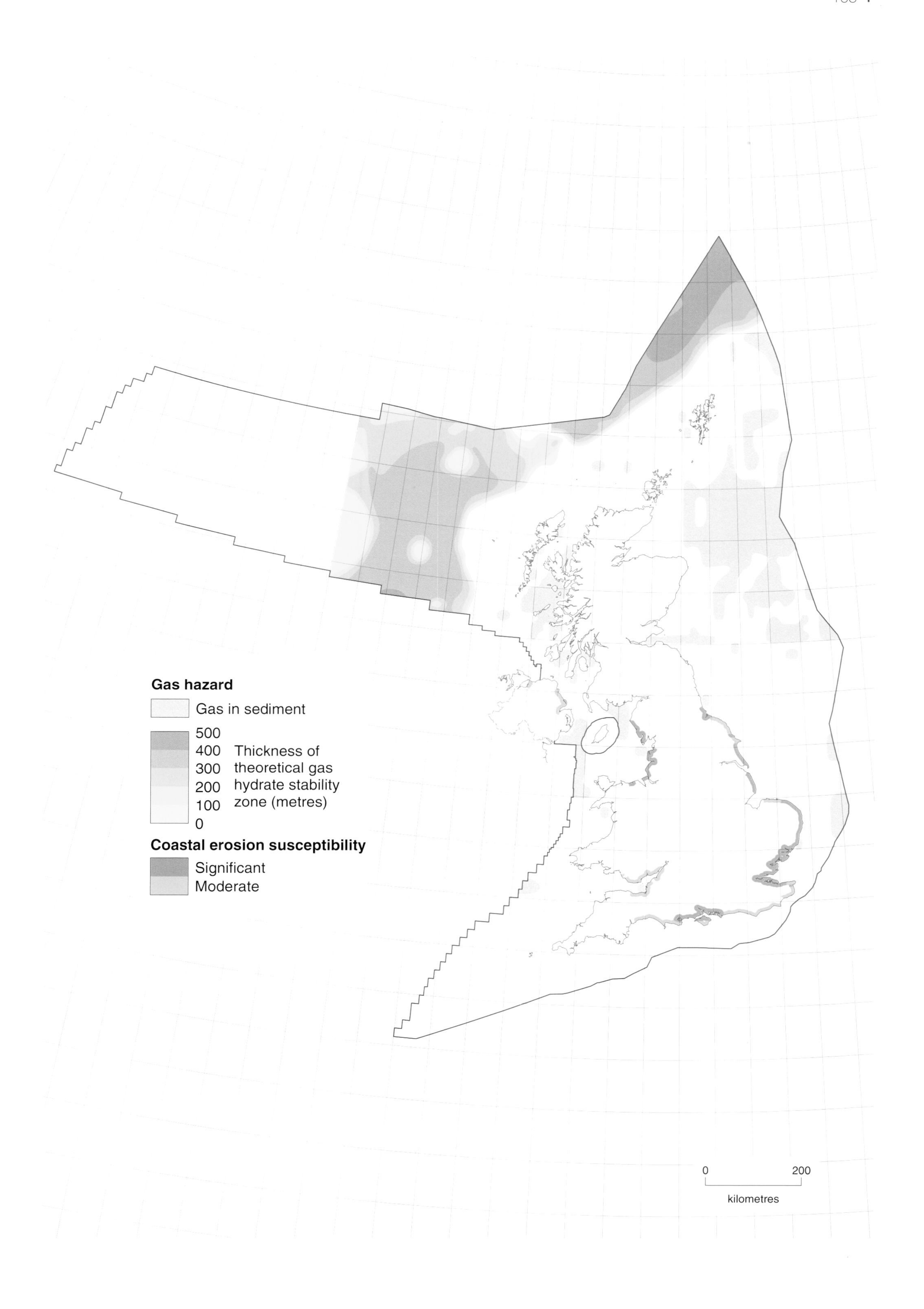

Gas hazard
Gas in sediment
500
400
300
200
100
0
Thickness of theoretical gas hydrate stability zone (metres)
Coastal erosion susceptibility
Significant
Moderate
0
200
kilometres

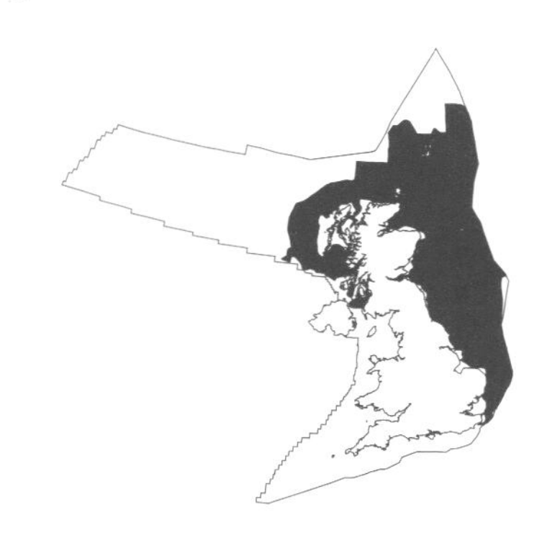

Offshore and coastal

Copper in sea bed sediment

Sea bed sediment consists of grains and particles that have been reworked from older strata, together with shells and organic material produced as a result of biological activity. Human activities on land and at sea also contribute to the variations in composition. The copper element distribution map, shown here, is one example of the analysis of the inorganic geochemistry of the sediment.

Most modern sea bed sediments are reworked from older sediments or rocks. Thus, variations in the inorganic geochemistry of the sea bed can be used in the study of water circulation patterns, sediment sources and transport, and can also be used to distinguish natural variations from those due to contamination. Sediment geochemistry may also be interpreted in terms of the different element concentrations associated with particular grain sizes.

Changes of element concentrations with time have been investigated by taking sea bed samples over a period of time, or by comparing the sea bed sediments with samples taken from below the sea bed. The geochemistry of the sediments from around the UK can be compared with published values worldwide. Geochemical data are used in prospecting for mineral and aggregate resources. The data are also helpful in assessing the effects of historical human activities, both onshore and offshore, and in monitoring the modern sea bed environment.

Geochemical data are available from analyses of sea bed samples that were collected between 1969 and 1986. Samples were taken at an average density of one sample per 43 square kilometres. The analytical results are based on sediments that are less than 2 millimetres in grain size. The results are stored in a digital database and are also available in the form of maps in which the data are represented statistically in relation to the grain size classifications of sea bed sediments, corrected for variation in the sediment constituents.

Aluminium
Barium
Beryllium
Bismuth
Boron
Cadmium
Copper
Chromium
Gallium
Iron
Lanthanum
Lead
Lithium
Magnesium
Manganese
Mercury
Nickel
Potassium
Rubidium
Silica
Strontium
Tin
Titanium
Uranium
Yttrium
Zinc
Zirconium

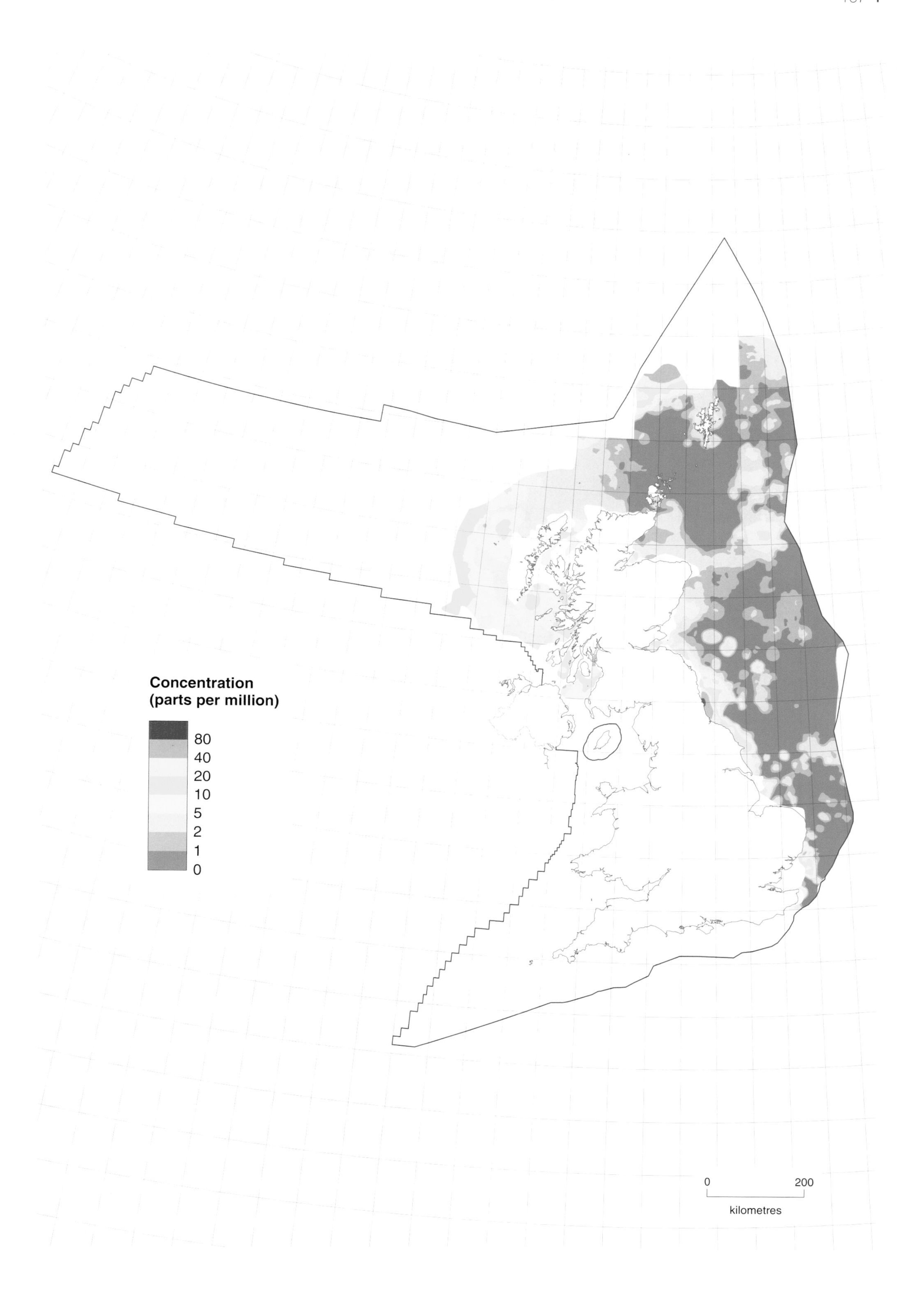
Concentration
(parts per million)
80
40
20
10
5
2
1
0
0
200
kilometres

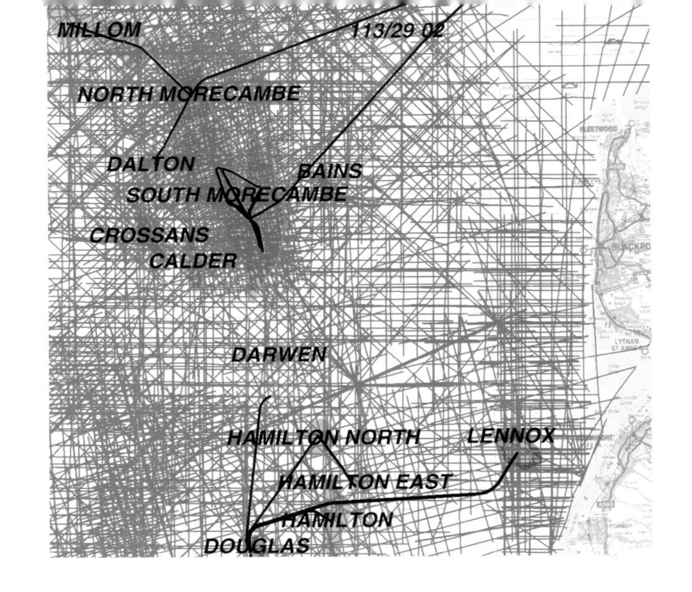

Offshore and coastal

Oil and gas

This map illustrates a selection of data on petroleum exploration and production around Britain. It shows the location of oil and gas fields, pipelines and the areas that were made available to be licensed for exploration during the 21st Round of Offshore Licensing. The data were extracted from the *DEAL Data Registry* for UK Offshore Oil and Gas, which allows access to data and information about offshore oil and gas exploration and production in the UK.

DEAL (Digital Energy Atlas and Library) catalogues link to sources of data, such as geophysical logs of exploration wells, well cores, seismic reflection data and geological reports, and provide downloads of selected reference data. Other information about the infrastructure of the offshore area is also available and includes the location of oil and gas industry installations, hazards and safety zones.

DEAL (www.ukdeal.co.uk) was developed by BGS, and is funded by Common Data Access Ltd, a wholly owned subsidiary of the UK Offshore Operators Association, with support from the Department of Trade and Industry.

BGS holds a wealth of primary and interpreted geological and geophysical data, which provide an essential scientific base for the exploration and development of the UK offshore area.

Pipeline
Oil or gas field
DTI blocks offered for licence, 21st round
0
200
kilometres

Britain beneath our feet

Obtaining the digital data

BGS wishes to encourage the fullest possible use of the data and information it holds; with the exception of confidential data, all BGS digital data and information are available for public and commercial use. Data are generally leased for a fee under a non-exclusive licence, which is renewable on an annual basis. Data used for educational purposes and academic research attracts a discounted rate.

In many cases the data and information described in this atlas can be made available 'off the shelf' as standard data files for unit areas. Alternatively, users may wish to specify the area and attributes they wish to receive. However, some of the information produced by BGS is highly specialised and bespoke data packages are the preferred method of delivery.

If you wish to know more about any of the data and information available from BGS, its detailed technical specification, coverage and cost, please contact the following address in the first instance:

Central Enquiries (Digital Licensing Enquiries)
British Geological Survey,
Keyworth, Nottingham
NG12 5GG
United Kingdom
Email: enquiries@bgs.ac.uk
Tel: +44 (0)115 936 3143
Fax: +44 (0)115 936 3615

If you simply wish to know about the geology and related information around where you live, then you may like to try a new BGS online service *www.bgs.ac.uk/georeports* that can provide information on entry of a postcode.

The web site *www.bgs.ac.uk* contains a wealth of information about the data held by BGS. Online *Geographical Information Systems* will allow you to search the BGS data catalogue spatially.

Ground magnetic survey across the Leven Schist

Britain beneath our feet

Acknowledgements

We acknowledge and wish to express our thanks to many organisations who have provided data and information to BGS over the years and without whom production of this atlas would not have been possible.

We would particularly like to record our gratitude to a number of individuals and organisations that have made a specific contribution:

Arup Ltd
Coal Authority
Common Data Access Ltd
Department of Trade and Industry
Environment Agency
Geological Survey of Canada
Greenwich Council
Hydrographic Office
Joe Cornish
John Gilmour
Lancashire Evening Post
National House-Building Council
Office of the Deputy Prime Minister
Ordnance Survey
Sealand Aerial Photography
Scottish Environmental Protection Agency
Scripps Institute of Oceanography
UK Offshore Oil Operators Association
University of Edinburgh

This atlas and the data behind it, are the products of the work of many BGS staff, both present and past. However, the following people have made a direct contribution to this book:

Production Team
Debbie Rayner
Russell Lawley
Tony Myers
Simon Rippon
Audrey Jackson
Marieta Garcia-Bajo
Alex Rotton
Jim Rayner
Fergus MacTaggart
John Arbon
Ian Cooke
Roger Parnaby
Sheila Myers
Jayne Kmieciak
Tim Cullen

Theme contributors
Don Appleton
Andrew Bloodworth
Neil Breward
Don Cameron
Barry Chacksfield
Greg Chapman
Stan Coats
Tim Colman
Alan Forster
Bob Gatliff
Dave Highley
Richard Holmes
Richard Hughes
Ewan Hyslop
Ceri James
Gareth Jenkins
Chris Johnson
Howard Johnson
David Kerridge
Geoff Kimbell
Gary Kirby
Dave Long
Graham Lott
Susan Macmillan
Andrew McKenzie
Roger Musson
Mike Petterson
Barry Rawlins
Derek Reay
John Rees
Keith Rollin
Susanne Sargeant
Kevin Smith
Glenn Thompson

Britain beneath our feet

The British Geological Survey

The BGS holds a wealth of information and knowledge acquired by the generations of geologists who have investigated the Britain beneath our feet. The combination of this information base and a unique range of geoscience expertise gives the BGS its key core competence.

The BGS is a public sector research establishment — a part of the Natural Environment Research Council (NERC) with links to Government through the Office of Science and Technology. We were established in 1835 to provide vital information on the nation's resources and the geological knowledge essential for the development of Britain's transport networks. Today, our survey and monitoring activities provide the scientific knowledge needed to understand engineering ground conditions, natural hazards, groundwater, petroleum and mineral resources and the impact of climate change. This knowledge is used in land use planning, coastal zone protection, CO_2 sequestration, pollution and waste management, and international development. We are a world leader in scientific data and information management and contribute, directly and indirectly, to more than £30 billion of economic activity each year. We receive an NERC Science Budget allocation of £21 million per year and earn a similar amount from research commissions. These commissions address the specific interests of government departments and agencies, local government and the private sector, in the UK and internationally.